THE CHEMICAL RELIGION

The Chemical Religion

The Truth
about
Drugs and Teens

by

Peter Turkel

PAULIST PRESS DEUS BOOKS

Glen Rock, N. J.   New York, N. Y.

Toronto   Amsterdam   London

Library of Congress
Catalog Card Number: 69-18371

Published by Paulist Press
Editorial Office: 304 W. 58th St., N. Y., N. Y. 10019
Business Office: Glen Rock, New Jersey 07452

Printed in the
United States of America
by Our Sunday Visitor Press

Contents

Introduction

WHY SHOULD you read this book? Perhaps you are fascinated by dangerous drugs. Or perhaps your classmates or teachers or parents or sons and daughters talk endlessly about "pot" and "acid" and you want to know the facts about these drugs. The chances are good that you have not yet "turned on" with marijuana or LSD. However, the chances are equally good that you know someone who has.

Drug abuse, in all its stark reality, has been taken from the distant slum and slammed down in the living room of every American home today. Teenagers and college youths want to know about these chemicals so readily available in school, at parties, at hangouts and even in their homes.

Lies and myths fabricated by well-meaning parents and teachers are no longer acceptable to today's youth. Any parent foolish enough to try such techniques is begging for trouble.

This book has one purpose—to tell the facts about the most used of today's dangerous drugs: LSD, marijuana, barbiturates, amphetamines, heroin and a few others. The author is a reporter, not a crusader determined to issue flat condemnations. The book is designed to equip parents and youth with the basic knowledge they must have in the hope that some hard thinking now will make protracted rehabilitation at some later date unnecessary.

It is a national disgrace that in this day and age an ever growing number of promising lives are being shattered in head-on collisions with chemicals. And as more and more young people seek to disentangle themselves from the wreckage of their youth, their pitiful pleas "But I didn't know" and "I didn't think" are being heard with increasing frequency.

Read! Think! Decide for yourself!

Here are the facts.

A Drugged Society

ONE THING is certain: ours is a drug-happy society. Almost every American uses some form of addictive. More than 70 million are no strangers to alcohol. More than that number smoke cigarettes, cigars or pipes. Nearly every adult in the United States drinks coffee, tea or hot chocolate, all of which contain caffeine.

Roots of the Problem

These addictives have been dubbed "acceptable" by society, and to these a new crutch was added in the 1950's. Today's student generation grew up in homes where drugs of all sizes, shapes and colors, in tablet, capsule or liquid form, were widely used to cure a wide variety of ills. Their parents took "happy pills" to set the mood for cocktail parties, pills to help them sleep, pills to relax them and pills to spark their energy.

Youths watched as medicine chests disgorged drugs designed to solve every personal problem, as well as every medical need. "It should not be surprising," one psychologist stated, "that some of them turn to drugs in order to escape the many problems with which our complex society confronts them." As Psychologist

3

Helen Nowlis of the University of Rochester told a Philadelphia gathering of student personnel administrators last year, in this pill age young people turn to drugs because of "curiosity, rebellion, the desire to improve social relations, to find a meaning in life [and] to be reborn."

This is one root of today's drug problem. After watching parents gulp the wonderdrug tranquilizers, young people decided that if these drugs were all right, no drug could be as dangerous as mom and dad claimed. Youngsters would give one ear to their parents' admonitions and then raid the medicine chest.

Another root is the boredom prevalent among today's youth, a boredom brought on by their parents' growing affluence. The middle class has mushroomed since World War II. New-found financial means made possible the vine-like spread of suburbia, with resultant attitudes of permissiveness and the desire to give the children everything the parents never had. There is no challenge to growing up when a silver platter is on hand to cater to every want.

Still another root is the vanishing of frontiers. Youth was left with little to challenge during non-school time. There was no need for a job, no sandlot to burn up energy—nothing but time to "hang out" with the gang, and nothing for that gang to seek but thrills and kicks.

One group of kids in the wealthy suburban town of Englewood Cliffs, New Jersey, sought their kicks by passing around bottles of airplane glue in a parking lot until a 12-year-old boy died, his insides burned out "as if by a blowtorch." Another group of pill-happy Long Island boys devised a plan to persuade their girl friends to join their kick so that, once high, they could be photographed in lewd poses. The boys then black-mailed the girls, aged 14 to 17, into submitting to them, and a prostitution ring was formed from which the boys reaped the profits.

Another factor, especially among the hippies or would-be hippies, is frustration—frustration with the Vietnam war, frustration with the prospect of finishing college to die in a rice paddy, frustration over the lack of challenges. The civil rights drive is no longer their crusade. They are bored and fed up with what they feel is a staid society without meaningful challenge. Drugs for them are but one facet of a growing subculture of defiance—defiance of the very ideals their parents hold sacred. They are tired of parental hypocrisy. If mom and dad use tranquilizers, alcohol, tobacco, coffee and a dozen other addictives, why, they ask, is marijuana banned? Why is LSD pounced upon? According to them, pot and acid are no more dangerous than the drugs their parents use. Why not seek a better world, they ask, a world of love and truth, by turning inward with a chemical assist? Couldn't drugs perhaps provide answers for the youth born in the nuclear age of constant turmoil?

Among the teeny boppers, often as young as 11 years old, the excuse for drug abuse has a far less philosophical basis. Most frequently it stems from fears of being labeled "chicken" or of being an outcast among their friends. The thought of rebellion, of doing something dad says mustn't be done, is often a beginning. This leads to experimentation in forbidden fields. "I started to drink cough medicine when I was 12," an 18-year-old heroin user admitted. "It was the thing to do. If you didn't drink with the older kids, you were a dead body."

What Is a User?

A few terms must be defined before going further. What is drug addiction? How does it differ from habituation? Is there such a thing as an occasional user?

Addiction is the chronic and continuous use of a drug to such an extent that a physical dependence on that drug results. Increasing amounts of the drug are needed to reproduce the same kick that was received when its use began, and a mental attitude develops that tells the mind: "I must have it." The opium drugs, including heroin, as well as barbiturates and some tranquilizers, fall in this grouping.

Habituation is largely psychological. The mind feels that it must have a particular drug which the body, for the most part, could take or leave. Marijuana falls in this category.

It is possible to be an intermittent drug user. In fact, most of today's youthful drug experimenters are in this class. They may use LSD, barbiturates, amphetamines, tranquilizers or cocaine at a party and not tangle with the drug for another month; however, they are in no less danger than a "regular."

Formerly, when one heard the phrase "drug user," the mind immediately pictured a slum-dwelling heroin addict. Today these addicts form the hard core of the nation's drug takers. However, heroin addicts—estimated at some 60,000 by the Federal Bureau of Narcotics but actually about triple that number—are only a tiny minority scattered among millions of drug users at all levels of society. They are found in small, usually run-down areas like New York's Tompkins Square Park. They spend nearly $400 million a year—most of it "earned" through burglary, prostitution and the sale of narcotics—for the white powder that rules their lives.

There is a world of difference between the hard-core user of heroin or morphine and the vast majority of today's drug-seeking youth. As one former resident of Harlem put it: "Slum kids never had anything and they will never have anything. They will live and die without hope on 125th Street. These kids look around, and whom do they see in the mohair suits and flashy cars? "The pusher, that's who! They see heroin as the only way for betterment. These kids have been promised so many programs—promises that were never kept. But the pusher is real. He's the king of society."

Drug abuse spreads from person to person. Pushers may not be lurking in the shadows ready to lure the unwary, but they are available to any youth who wants to make a purchase.

Glues, cough syrups and pills are easily available to today's youth, and it is only slightly more difficult for them to obtain marijuana and LSD. As for heroin, some friend always seems to know a friend who knows a guy who sells it.

An essential fact to remember is that the taking of drugs is a voluntary act. You can't catch addiction the way you catch a cold. Those blackmailed girls *agreed* to take the pills. Whether you volunteer or not depends on you. And you can't decide unless you know what these drugs are, what they can do, who uses them, and why.

Death and
Squiggly Toothpaste

A QUIET, fog-shrouded cemetery in Greenwich, Connecticut, received the severely battered remains of 18-year-old Linda Rae Fitzpatrick shortly after the Rev. Bradford Hastings had conducted a simple, 15-minute service without any eulogy at Christ Episcopal Church.

The nude bodies of the pretty, chestnut-haired daughter of a wealthy spice importer and her hippie boyfriend, 21-year-old James Hutchinson, were found ten feet apart in the blood-spattered boiler room of an East Village tenement in the heart of New York's LSD-motivated hippieland. They were lying face down on a dirty concrete floor with their heads smashed in. A brick wrapped in a pair of men's trousers was believed to have been the death weapon.

Linda's flirtation with the hippie world ended in death about 1 A.M. on Sunday, October 8, 1967. She was buried the following Tuesday, the day after an unmarried drifter and a laborer who is married and has a child were charged with homicide. The laborer, 26-year-old Don Ramsey, a bearded, fez-wearing follower of a primitive African religion, told police that the slaying followed an LSD party in the boiler room where

Linda was raped four times. "I had taken some LSD; I was really flying," Ramsey was quoted as saying. "I saw spots and colors and whirling things and heard bells going off."

According to the police, Linda had told her family that she was on her way to San Francisco to visit her brother. Instead she headed for Greenwich Village where, according to the unmarried drifter, 26-year-old Thomas Dennis, Linda and her long-haired boyfriend—nicknamed "Groovy" because he really made the scene among fellow hippies—had organized an LSD or "acid" party on the eve of her murder. Linda was described as an aspiring artist who was both fascinated and frightened by hippieland. Hutchinson—pictured by an army of his hippie friends as part saint, part comedian and all heart—was her protector.

Linda's brutal death caused another shock wave in the tension-filled world of the worried parents of teenagers and college youths. Parents generally know how to handle the problems caused by booze blasts, juvenile delinquency and even forays into sex, but they can't cope with diethylamide of lysergic acid, the H-bomb of the psychedelic (mind-manifesting) drugs, or with marijuana, the basic crutch of the hippie or psychedelic movement.

The World of LSD

LSD sprang from a Swiss test tube in 1938 and swept the nation's curious youth on a crest of laudatory magazine articles and books after 1963. What is this drug? What does it do? What is the movement it has spawned? These questions affect nearly every American home, and they demand cold, hard facts.

Since LSD seeped from the hands of clinical researchers into the hands of youth it has been the subject of controversy. One auburn-haired coed popped an LSD-doused sugar cube into her mouth and let it dissolve. Thirty minutes later she entered an impossibly beautiful, swirling new world of starkly vivid blues, reds and yellows as she stared at a simple abstract painting. Sound from her stereo squiggled toward her "like toothpaste" as a feeling of well-being enveloped her mind. Suddenly she had the answers to her hangups. She had found the key to living. But another undergraduate discovered to his utter terror that he had no flesh, no bones, no body. Instead, he was a screaming mass of multi-colored worms. Still another huddled in a Los Angeles hospital psychiatric ward convinced he was an orange that would squirt juice if touched.

These reactions—one a good LSD experience or "trip," the other two the result of a bad trip or "freakout"—form the essence of the controversy. According to Dr. James L. Goddard, former U.S. Food and Drug Administrator, taking LSD is "like playing Russian roulette on a sugar cube." However, the LSD cult's high priest, ex-Harvard psychologist Dr. Timothy Leary, is convinced otherwise. He declared: "LSD has an eerie power to release ancient energies from the human brain—I would say sacred energies."

The great debate continues to rage, with fearful parents and curious youth caught in the middle. Although LSD users ("acidheads") talk in terms of religious ecstasy, creative fulfillment, do-it-yourself psychotherapy, political freedom and love, psychiatrists and biochemists provide an ever increasing flood of reports about permanent mental and physical damage. Some of these reports tell of hospitals packed with LSD-caused schizophrenics, while others offer conclusive evidence that key blood cells have been impaired seriously enough to cause brain damage or malformation in the children of acidheads.

A great deal of misinformation has obscured the known facts about LSD. The final reports have yet to be completed, but medical researchers and psychiatrists, some under U.S. government grants, are conducting intense investigations. Their findings, printed with increasing frequency in medical journals, offer incontrovertible evidence about mental and physical damage.

What Is LSD?

Let's get down to bedrock facts. Diethylamide of lysergic acid is a colorless, odorless, tasteless and technically non-addictive drug that "expands consciousness" by working on the central nervous system. It is one of several psychedelics that include marijuana, peyote, mescaline, psilocybin (sacred mushroom), DMT, STP, morning glory seeds and nutmeg (the last two require special preparation).

Chemist Albert Hofmann discovered LSD quite by accident as he was conducting experiments at the laboratories of Sandoz, Ltd., in Basel, Switzerland, in an effort to find useful new compounds of ergot, a fungus that attacks rye kernels. However, his attention was turned to other tasks before he could put LSD through the routines of lab testing. But on April 16, 1943 he returned to the vial, and somehow a speck of it entered his system. "I was seized by a peculiar restlessness associated with mild dizziness," he wrote in his journal. "I lay down and sank into a kind of activity of the imagination. . . . There surged upon me an uninterrupted stream of fantastic images of extraordinary plasticity and vividness, accompanied by an intense, kaleidoscopic play of colors."

Dr. Hofmann continued his research, and four years later he recorded his first freakout: "I felt as if I were out of my body. I thought I had died. My 'ego' was suspended somewhere in space and I saw my body lying dead on the sofa. I observed and registered clearly that my 'alter ego' was moving around the room, moaning." Sandoz gathered samples of Hofmann's weird new compound with the power to make the mind do somersaults and sent them to universities around the world for research.

In the 1950's, LSD and other hallucinogenic compounds were studied extensively because they were thought to produce symptoms similar to those caused by schizophrenia. It was hoped that LSD would serve the age-old technique of artificially producing a disease in order to find a cure of the affliction itself. However. it is now known that LSD symptoms are significantly different from those found in schizophrenics. Perceptual distortions produced by LSD are not typical of the malady, even though the depersonalization caused by the acid can be found in acute schizophrenics.

Meanwhile, at Atlantic City, New Jersey, a meeting of the American Psychiatric Association was held. Present was Aldous Huxley, the philosopher, novelist and lover of science, who had taken mescaline, a hallucogen milder than LSD. His address to the assembled psychiatrists was destined to filter into every American home where parents, until then, had only to worry about little things like juvenile delinquency. Huxley stated: "The almost magical power exercised by certain works of art springs from the fact that they remind us—consciously or, more often, unconsciously—of that other world which the natural visionary can enter at will, and to which the rest of us have access only under the influence of hypnosis or a drug such as mescaline or LSD."

The Spread of LSD

Huxley merely introduced the possibilities of expanding one's mental horizons with LSD. It was left to a young firebrand psychologist, Timothy Leary of Harvard University's Center for Research in Personality, to seize upon this almost science-fiction idea and turn it into a controversial national movement. Leary had heard of the exotic experiences available from psilocybin, and while vacationing in Mexico in the summer of 1960, he took the nibble of the "sacred mushroom" that launched the psychedelic movement.

At the age of 39, Leary told *Playboy* magazine, "my joy in life, my sensual openness, my creativity were all sliding downhill. I was a middle-aged man involved in the middle-aged process of dying." But after eating some of the mushroom, within minutes he was "swept over the edge of a sensory Niagara into a maelstrom of transcendental vision and hallucinations. It was above all and without question the deepest religious experience of my life."

That fall, Dr. Tim, as LSD users or acidheads affectionately call him, visited Huxley at nearby M.I.T. and discussed the author's belief that hallucinations could perform a radical self-transcendence and provide a deeper understanding of the nature of things. Then, his imagination fired, Leary convinced psychologist Richard Alpert to join him, and over the next two years, the two of them probed the uncharted depths of psilocybin and LSD. They utilized students as subjects for their experiments, despite warnings from Harvard officials that testing in an unclinical atmosphere without medical help on hand was too dangerous and too uncertain.

Until Leary and Alpert appeared on the scene, LSD trials were confined to cold laboratory conditions where the effect was more of anxiety than happiness. But Dr. Tim took psychedelics into the warm, familiar surroundings of homes. He added flowers, music and art—designed, supposedly, to set the mood for meaningful consciousness-expanding.

Some 3,500 doses of psilocybin later, the storm clouds over Harvard burst. Alpert was fired, charged with breaking an agreement not to test psychedelics on undergraduates. Leary was suspended for his extended absences from the campus.

Subsequently, Dr. Tim found an angel for a few years in millionaire William M. Hitchcock. From Hitchcock's 4,000-acre estate in Millbrook, New York, Leary made countless forays to preach his gospel of chemical mysticism. His knack for devising the catchy phrase enchanted the press. Almost every pronouncement he made was headline material: "Leary Says LSD Opens Way to Greater Self-Understanding." "Leary Says LSD Increases Artistic Ability." "Leary Says LSD Boosts Spiritual Life." The psychedelic movement was on.

The acid message spread from the hippies of San

Francisco's Haight-Ashbury district to New York's East Village and to thousands of big campuses and little towns in between. Cores of dedicated LSD users, whose dress, affectation and far-out style sparked the imagination and rebellious nature of youth, spread their message in ever widening circles of young, intellectually-minded students and curious kids.

In 1963, the same year that Leary and Harvard parted company, the American Medical Association warned that research had demonstrated "beyond question" that LSD "has the power to damage the individual psyche and perhaps to cripple it for life." But the acid cult couldn't have cared less about such warnings. A goodly number of them had already eaten a sugar cube, pill or "spitball" containing 100 micrograms or 1/10,000 of a gram of LSD, had suffered no ill effects and had unquestionably enjoyed the experience.

That New-Time
Religion

IN ADDRESSING a sellout crowd at the New York Athletic Club, ex-Catholic Timothy Leary, the high priest or guru of LSD, declared: "Like every great religion of the past, we seek to find the divinity within, and to express this revelation in a life of glorification and worship of God. . . . These ancient goals we define in the metaphor of the present: turn on, tune in and drop out."

The prophet of religion through chemistry then went on to announce the formation of the League for Spiritual Discovery (the initials are no accident) and to explain the rallying cry: "*Turn on* means to go beyond your secular tribal level to contact the many levels of divine energy which lie within your consciousness. *Tune in* means to express and to communicate your new revelations in visible acts of glorification, gratitude and beauty. *Drop out* means to detach yourself harmoniously, tenderly and gracefully from worldly commitments until your entire life is dedicated to worship and search."

The League for Spiritual Discovery

One basic reason Leary "turned on" the League for

Spiritual Discovery was to give shape and meaning to psychedelic experience. He asserted that without guidance and meditation, the spiritual energies supposedly released by LSD would be wasted, and the experience would be simply one of pleasure-seeking. League members were to use LSD, marijuana and peyote as "sacramentals" before "shrines" in the homes, turning on with acid once a week and with pot daily.

Leary is one of the more sensational leaders of the psychedelic movement, whose full-time members are called "hippies" after the "hip" beatniks of the 1950's. Among others are the British rock group, the Beatles, and Indian sitar expert Ravi Shankar whose folk tunes of India have an eerie "psychedelic" or mind-manifesting sound.

Though respect for Leary is now sagging, his views on better living through chemistry have attracted a large number of college and high school students who flatly reject the dearly held beliefs of what Leary calls the "whiskey-drinking, middle-class, middle-brow, middle-aged people."

Research psychologist William H. McGlothlin of the University of California at Los Angeles, traveled the length and breadth of California to study the acid cult for the National Institute of Mental Health. He reported that "the value system of the hippies of the LSD movement is quite like the early days of Christianity, which proposes loving cooperation and deemphasizes wealth and material gain."

Leary, looking very much like the early Christian with his beard, long white gown and bare feet, has repeatedly stated that the "only point in life is the religious quest. Find your own divinity within yourself."

The League for Spiritual Discovery conducts its quest in a shabby store on the lower west side of Manhattan. As the glass door, adorned with notices of lectures, was opened, this reporter was enveloped in incense and his ears were battered by a plaintive Hindu chant which undulated through the dim light. From somewhere a sitar whined over hushed, mumbling voices.

Eight of Dr. Tim's faithful adherents squatted, lounged or sat on the meditation room's wildly colored rugs trying to drop into unity with their environments. Nan, a rail of a girl in a bulky green sweatshirt and faded blue jeans, carefully put down the daisy that was holding her attention and rose to ask me to remove my shoes. Then she led me by the hand to the center's other room, used for decompression, and whispered that some of the faithful were using the sacramentals. One college type had his eyes rigidly fixed on a Buddha.

Nan explained that the center gives instruction in the proper administration of LSD. A proper diet of mostly grains, sound mental preparation and an awareness of Eastern philosophy were recommended. An object to focus attention upon during a trip is also important. "Set and setting are essential," she declared. The center has available a series of "trip books," each designed to guide the acidhead on his voyage to inner space. One of the books depicts children playing in a park. It is designed to inspire a childlike attitude of love for all. According to Nan, careful programming and proper settings prevent the horrors of freakouts.

A tall blond youth, attired in a grey turtleneck pullover decked with beads, injected the thought that programming a trip can also be directed toward a goal.

For instance, he explained, trip books could be used to create a political atmosphere that would make the reader a militant advocate of peace in Vietnam.

Nan and I then left the League center for a run-down East Village brownstone where several other hippies explained their religion. The dimly lit pad was crowded with a mass of sweaty young people strewn among mattresses haphazardly placed on the floor.

"Christ was outside the Establishment and what did they do to him?" asked a New York University drop-out. "Christ was talking about human beings who have a right to exist in their own way." She then went on to a defense of the hippie communal life. Anyone was free to come in and sleep on the mattresses, bathe in the unprivate tub and dip a spoon into the stew pot. Another girl, nicknamed "Horse" because she once pranced about neighing, declared: "I'm not breaking God's laws. I'm breaking man's laws, and some of them are wrong. I believe J. C. will take care of us."

LSD and Religion

Both Leary and his first disciple, Alpert, have described at length how LSD supposedly liberated them from their Establishment hangups and set them in tune with the universe and their fellow man. Such beliefs are not without historical precedent. The "shrewbread" of the Bible was believed to confer the gift of prophecy on priests. Mexican Indians still use "sacred mushrooms" to produce ecstatic states. Their predecessors, the Aztecs, used those mushrooms while offering human sacrifice to their gods. In the American Southwest, Navajo Indians, among others, legally use peyote in their worship as members of the Native American

Church. "White men talk about Jesus," they say. "We talk to Jesus."

Leary's cultists draw inspiration from all religions and attempt to expand it chemically. However, his critics charge that he is given undue respect as a man of the cloth. Catholic, Protestant and Jewish leaders almost universally damn the claims of the high priest of acidheads.

Rev. Anthony Bosko, vice-chancellor of the Pittsburgh Catholic diocese, states flatly: "I don't believe in religious aphrodisiacs. If I am to love God, I must love him with my whole conscious heart."

According to Dr. Robert Bruce Pierce of the First Methodist Church in Chicago, Leary's religion is no different than erotic rites where ancient men "built religion around emotional and sensual experiences that were largely sexual."

The Rev. Henry V. Malcolm, Presbyterian minister at Columbia University, New York, thinks that it is reasonably accurate to characterize Leary's faith as a religion inasmuch as "the person on a trip is recapturing his history in the same way religion does with symbolism, like communion—a primitive act of cannibalism." He adds, however, that "LSD is simply another form of esthetization, not an answer, to the problems of social change."

Rabbi Joseph S. Shubow of Temple B'nai Moshe, Boston, bluntly asserts: "This is a satanic, terrifying and tormenting temptation to man to look into worlds that may destroy his own world."

David Graubart of Chicago, the presiding rabbi of the ecclesiastical court of the Chicago Rabbinical Assembly, comments: "We feel that the hallucinatory approach is non-intellectual and non-mystical."

Chicago theologian Martin E. Marty refuses to put down the thousands of hippies who follow the teachings of Leary and others as creative misfits. He sees them as spiritually motivated crusaders striking out at society's lack of a soul.

The hippies' Christian message of love for all, a message characterized by their irreverence for the established norms of society, went out from the East Village in New York and San Francisco's Haight-Ashbury district to campuses and school grounds across the country. It reached Laurie, a 16-year-old strawberry blonde with light blue eyes, through magazine articles and newspaper stories. It was the major topic of conversation in her Lincoln, Nebraska, high school.

Laurie had seen psychedelic advertising, posters and art. She had heard the weird tones of the new rock music which contained messages that her mother was incapable of understanding, and she loved to wear the psychedelically-inspired clothes that proclaimed the freedom of youth. Finally, she decided to catch the scene herself. With a few dollars tucked in her pocket and an underground newspaper to guide her, she arrived on Haight Street and smiled. The hippies smiled back, in a way that people in Lincoln never did. And that is why she came.

Laurie and
Her Friends

LAURIE had been brought up in a pleasant suburban home. Her parents had hoped that after college she would marry a rising young businessman and take up the comfortable middle-class life they loved. In effect, Laurie had everything her parents never had, yet she rejected such a life. She dropped out and fled in search of an identity of her own. She thought she might find it in the world of love about which she had read, talked and heard so much.

A recently released four-year study of students at Stanford and the University of California contains some keys to the attitude of Laurie and older college youths who drop out into the hippie world. The project, directed by research psychologist Joseph Katz, concludes that college years are miserable, fraught with loneliness, sexual famine and uncertainty about direction. The majority of students questioned, when asked what interests and activities in college life were most important to them, gave high ratings to "career," "love and affection," "developing a personal identity" and "time for thinking and reflection."

22

Laurie and Steve

Laurie's long, straight hair blew gently in the breeze as she stood on a corner of Ashbury Street, in the center of a 100-square-block district of three-story Tudor and Victorian homes bordering lush Golden Gate Park. She gazed down the four blocks of Haight Street that form the hippie business district. Colorful shops smelled of incense; their walls were covered with posters condemning the war and praising pot. Counters were loaded down with hippie-made psychedelic jewelry, beads and clothing. Photos of long dead film stars were for sale, as well as a mass of somewhat worn mateless shoes. Music came from all sides—the Beatles, folk, African, played on sitars, guitars, tambourines, flutes and drums.

Laurie moved through a mass of sandled, bearded, beaded and long-haired humanity. Brilliant pink and red curlicued letters on a poster proclaimed: "Don't Say Love; Do It!" She waded through Mao Tse Tung coats, Mexican chalecos, Oriental robes, Indian costumes and Puritan attire to a bulletin board used for inter-hippie communication.

It was Laurie's first night in the national capital of hippiedom. She was accepted immediately, without question. There she met Steve, from Brooklyn, whose wide brown eyes turned her on. Clean-shaven with extra long hair, he was dressed in old blue jeans and a slightly unraveled sweater. Steve took Laurie to a communal pad overlooking the Panhandle of Golden Gate Park that juts eight blocks into Hashbury.

Steve had run smack into the psychedelic movement two years before, when he was 17. A high school acquaintance had invited him to a party of "real swingers" where he was introduced to the teachings of hippiedom and LSD. Immediately attracted, he began staying away from home all night to travel on the acid express. School, he thought, was a boring waste of time and completely pointless. His major interest was art and he wanted to devote more time to it. His hair grew longer as his paintings more and more began to depict brooding eyes peering through psychedelic hazes.

Steve's parents, who constantly lectured him about bathing, wearing clean clothes, skipping school, missing dinner and a million other things, became a drag. Finally he dragged his art books and little else to the Port Authority Bus Terminal and went west.

Steve furnished Laurie with a mattress under a sign that read "Praise the Pill—Bless Our Pad." Her new home was crowded with unequal numbers of boys and girls who split from home before her.

Laurie soon found that all things were shared in a hippie commune—not just food, money, LSD and sexual favors, but also infectious hepatitis, resulting from communal needles, and venereal disease (up more than six times the normal rate since the hippie influx). Luckily Laurie avoided the last two.

The Hippies

Though figures are a "down trip"—in other words, boring—to hippies, the best estimates conclude that there are 10,000 in San Francisco and another 6,000 in New York's East Village. Thousands of "plastic" or weekend hippies swarm among the boutiques, button shops and discotheques in hippie enclaves in every major city from Boston to Seattle and from Montreal to New Orleans. Hippies themselves estimate that they number about 300,000 nationwide, including those who only drop out for a weekend.

The hippies, who turned their backs on their past to seek the soul that society lost in its rush to affluence, are predominantly white. "Negroes have nothing, so they don't need to drop out," one hippie explained. For the most part, hippies are middle-class, educated youths ranging in age from 17 to 25. Raised in the period of the civil rights movement and anti-Vietnam protests, they believe that respect for authority is relative, and they came to the low-rent, low-price hippie districts to give the word "love" real meaning and to awaken the nation to the hypocrisy of violence and prejudice in a country dedicated to peace and equality. However, their noble idea of creative community, implanted by the prophets of acid, became lost in a swirl of blinding colors and ear-splitting sound. LSD often became an end instead of a means.

The hippies consider society's present institutions to be ridiculous. To them political protest is absurd. Far more effective than demonstrations, in their view, is a living protest, one that devises new standards of individual conduct and new kinds of social organizations, and they put those ideas into practice.

According to hippies, what could be more ridiculous than:

—a morning bus carrying persons to work who don't talk or smile but who merely stare at their newspaper;

—a father who sees his children only two hours nightly, provided that he's not tied up at the office;

—a shower when one isn't really dirty.

Hippies believe that they are generating a new

society rich in spiritual grace. They preach altruism, mysticism, honesty, joy and non-violence. One irreverent reference to violence in a hippie sign cautioned: "Military Service May Be Hazardous to Your Health."

Hippies have been nicknamed "flower children" because of the obvious pleasure they take in draping themselves and their detractors in flowers at their "happenings." They have an almost childlike fascination for such things as beads, flowers and children that the square world takes for granted.

What Is the Significance of the Hippie Movement?

The all-embracing love for friend and foe alike is a key to the wide appeal of the hippie movement. As Dr. McGlothlin said in his report to the National Institute of Mental Health: "The hippies have taken what the humanists have been saying and are carrying it all the way." LSD cultists are seeking to scrap the achievement-oriented society and its competitiveness and create a society based charity for fellow man— a society, incidentally, that in many ways corresponds amazingly to the concepts of Pope Paul VI as outlined in his encyclical *Progressio Populorum*. According to McGlothlin, hippies serve as devil's advocates to underscore the inconsistencies and the hypocrisy in society, "those blind spots hard to see from within the Establishment."

Allan Katzman, editor of the *East Village Other,* the tabloid newspaper of New York's hippies, believes that the hippies are the forerunners of the future where technology will render work unnecessary. They want to learn to use this leisure time meaningfully and creatively. However, historian Arnold Toynbee sees the hippie movement as a revolt against the conformism that he believes has characterized American society since 1776. Toynbee's analysis states: "The question is whether, like St. Francis, the hippies are going to transfigure a defiant voluntary poverty into something positive, creative and redeeming. Only this could remold the American way of life."

One of the most striking things about the hippie movement is the way it has fired the imagination of the staid society against which it rebelled. Hippie slang is already in common usage, and the clothing available in any department store and the revolutionary trends in television advertising clearly indicate the great extent of the psychedelic influence.

The hippies are convinced that LSD has opened their minds to insights that will profit the whole of society. However, for many, acid has become an end in itself. Although their text, *The Psychedelic Experience* by Leary and others, showed them that LSD could serve as a stepping stone to get out of the environment, look at it objectively and create a new order, many have just dropped out without going further.

But finding new values to replace discarded ones can be a long and painful process, as the hippies have discovered. At first their movement was a flight from society to cut the bonds of hangups over the draft, sex and nuclear war by chemical means. Many stopped at the next stage and made acid their whole world. A few now have taken a third step, back toward a "straight" world molded to hippie standards.

The hippies have their own job placement office, a

free store where a hippie can deposit his worn clothes and walk out in "new" ones, free feedings in the park, their own newspapers and homes to house their numbers. Their community in San Francisco now includes a theater group, free plays in the park, a housing agency, at least 25 businesses and a "happening" house for free lectures and discussion groups.

To support their way of life, many hippie communes have formed their own "industries." Some 300 handicraft operations produce goods for hippie stores. These range from individual enterprises—e.g., girls who make a single dress a week—to an entire commune engaged in making hand-tooled handbags.

Psychedelic publications bring the hippie message to their own members as well as to curious tourists. The monarch of hippie newspapers is the *Oracle;* it is poetic, ecstatic and mystical, and about 100,000 copies of each edition are sold.

In New York's East Village, the members of Group Image—a collection of some 50 hippies, mostly from the Midwest—produce and sell everything from silk-screen prints to artifacts. Among the most popular items they offer are lapel pins made from plaster casts of their own navels. They have their own magazine, *Innerspace,* and a combo that plays at discotheques.

The rural commune is the latest concept among hippies in their attempt to build their society outside society. Some 30 of these rural communes are now in existence, mostly in the Midwest and Southwest. They provide a refuge for hippies who are fleeing from the commercialism of their own movement and from the criminals of the run-down hippie districts who find the flower children easy prey for rape, robbery and murder.

It was on such a farm commune that Laurie was last seen. She was off acid; she said she had passed beyond that stage. She was doing her thing for the commune, sewing a wildly colorful dress which would be sold in a San Francisco hippie shop. Others worked to supply vegetables to their city-dwelling fellow hippies.

Steve never reached this phase. He freaked out. Before police pulled him out of the path of a passing car, he had been screaming to friends during an LSD trip that his eyes were on his forehead and that his face was twisted and wildly distorted. He was judged to be definitely psychotic by psychiatrists and placed in a mental institution; the doctors there fear he may have suffered brain damage.

The plastic hippies and their younger understudies, the teeny boppers who are as young as 11 years old, jam the streets of hippiedom after school, at night and on weekends. They gyrate in dance rites to ear-rending music and seek doses of LSD and sticks of pot so that they may be like real hippies. They only skim the surface of the acid scene, but all too frequently they get burned.

Whatever their status—hard-core hippie, plastic hippie or teeny bopper—all these young people share a mutual danger that can ruin their lives if not blast them into insanity altogether. That danger is a sugar cube, pill, wad of paper or any other suitable substance soaked in LSD.

Destination:
Paradise or Hell?

MIKE screamed, "My brains are leaking out again," as he flung his sweaty body upright from a filthy mattress in a Haight-Ashbury hippie pad and staggered to the cracked bathroom mirror. "It won't stay buttoned," he cried. Brushing aside his matted hair, Mike slammed an open hand across his temple and whimpered: "The button's too loose. They keep oozing out."

Mike had been off acid for two months, but he was still on a trip. He was convinced that he had a button-down flap on his temple that refused to stay shut, allowing his reasoning power to trickle down his face. His trip was halted, at least momentarily, by a psychiatrist's reassurance that his flap was "nicely buttoned now."

His mind crazed by his LSD experience, Mike had freaked out. Crack-ups on the acid express are an ever present danger, even for those who have flown safely during dozens of trips. No user is immune. For the Mikes who blow their cool, LSD becomes a living hell that they will never forget. The others, who have been more fortunate in their use of acid, claim that it provides the greatest experience of their creative life or that it serves as a substitute for lost religious faith.

30

The LSD Experience

What is there in one-millionth of an ounce of this liquid that turns a sugar cube into an inner-space vehicle of heaven for some and hell for others? What does an acidhead experience for his dose that has cost him anywhere from three to five dollars? Who are the acidheads? Even more importantly, why are these people acidheads? The answers to these questions should serve as a flashing danger signal to would-be trip takers.

The psychotic episode that LSD launches "normally" lasts from eight to ten hours. Soon after LSD is taken, the heart beats faster, the hand trembles ever so slightly and the pupils of the eyes dilate considerably —one reason why many acidheads wear sunglasses even at night.

Then the acid express gathers speed. Changes in perception occur. Sensations overwhelm the mind. Dull colors suddenly jump with life; they become extremely vivid and flow and swirl in ceaseless motion. Objects melt into each other, then move apart. Colors suddenly have sound and sound has color. A sense of intense isolation and out-of-being develops—one major reason for freakouts.

The tripster can recognize the objects he sees, but he cannot concentrate upon them. His ability to think about what he sees is impaired as his mind wanders. Afterward he may recall his experience or black it out entirely. During the trip, the taker is usually uncommunicative. However, reactions vary widely, depending on the individual.

LSD-induced perceptual changes are responsible for

many of the claims that the drug increases creativity
and enhances one's ability to solve problems.

Dr. Keith Ditman, a psychiatrist at the Neuropsychiatric Institute of the University of California at Los
Angeles, has taken an LSD trip to find out "what people were talking about." "The feelings I got from
listening to music and looking at art were greatly intensified. I discerned things I never have before," he said
in a *New York Times* interview. "LSD doesn't give
anyone talent," he continued. "It gives them appreciation. I think I have a new dimension—an awakening,
aesthetic appreciation I didn't have before."

Dr. Sidney Cohen of the Wadsworth Veterans
Administration Hospital, Los Angeles, writing in the
Psychiatric Journal, detailed the intensified feelings
Ditman experienced: "Everything glows with a luminos-
ity of its own and texture becomes three-dimensional.
There is a tendency to dwell upon the minute, a fleck on
the wall, the grain of a piece of wood. Flowers open and
close as though the fine adjustment of a microscope
were being manipulated. . . . A face can rapidly alter
in expression and appearance so that a succession of
changing faces is perceived."

While most LSD users try to program their experiences by equipping their flight pads with selected props,
the props themselves can become like ink blots in a
Rorschach test. The user knows what he is looking at,
but he can conjure up all kinds of shapes and forms
simply by observing them.

After former osteopath Irene Hickman of Sacra-
mento, California, took LSD, she reported: "I saw
myself as a greasy spot on wet pavement with rainbow

hues. . . . I thought: 'If it breaks, I'll be destroyed—but so what.'"

Acidheads claim that the Mikes with unbuttoned flaps just don't know how to use the potent mind manipulator, and they reserve special scorn for the psychiatrists who try to have a true acid experiences in cold, clinical surroundings.

How Widespread Is the Use of LSD?

This very disrespect for freakouts and psychiatrists is one reason why so many turn on with LSD. High priest Leary has claimed that fully a third of the nation's college students are tuned in to acid. Dr. Donald B. Louria of New York's Bellevue Hospital, a man of vast experience with LSD's victims, scoffs at this claim, asserting his belief that "no more than 1% of the college students are using LSD." But even Louria's 1% is considerable. Translated, it comes out to 20,000 collegians.

The number using LSD may have reached a peak out late in 1966. Louria noted a 50% decline in users, based on admissions to Bellevue's psychiatric ward, and commented: "The kids realize that the long-range effects of LSD are considerable." Dr. Walter Tietz, a psychiatrist at County General Hospital, Los Angeles, said that after a peak was reached in June, 1966 with one user admitted a day, the number of acid victims has declined steadily to the point where now the hospital admits an average of two per week.

After an 18-month survey of California high schools, Dr. Duke D. Fisher and Dr. J. Thomas Ungerleider, both of the Department of Psychiatry at the UCLA Center for the Health Sciences, said that LSD use was admitted by anywhere from 3% to 30% of the students, depending upon the school. *Campus,* the student newspaper at the City College of New York, polled 286 undergraduates and found that 13—or a little over 4%—had used LSD at least once. *Guide Posts,* the student paper at North High School, Great Neck, Long Island, questioned 2,587 students in two local high schools. Of the 10th, 11th and 12th graders, 2% admitted trying LSD.

Who Are the Acidheads?

More important than mere numbers, however, are the acidheads themselves. Who are they? Why do they turn on?

The vast bulk of acidheads are of college age, generally from a middle-class environment and vaguely artistic. They seek the drug for kicks, to ease their emotional hangups or to find new, mystical or unknown experiences.

Two psychiatrists at Kings County Hospital, Brooklyn, recently reported that LSD use is now spreading to high school dropouts. Dr. Lewis Glickman and Dr. Michael Blumenfield reported their findings, based on 25 admissions over a nine-month period, in the July 1967 issue of the *New York State Journal of Medicine.*

The largest body of LSD users are those who seek the drug because they are faced with an "identity crisis," asserts Dr. Frank Barron, research psychologist at the University of California, Berkeley. He told an international conference on LSD in San Francisco that LSD users can be divided into seven categories. His listing included those who seek aesthetic appreciation, a religious experience, a cure for alcoholism and relief from personal psychological problems of a neurotic sort, as well as "seriously disturbed persons who are potentially suicidal or psychotic." According to Barron, many adolescents "turn to LSD in the hope that it will tell them something about themselves and will help to clarify the possibilities for future development."

The tragic human-torch death of a 24-year-old Beverly Hills girl may have been the result of this problem-solving through chemistry. Nancy Moore walked into a Los Angeles gas station on July 4, 1966, placed a picture of a bearded Indian religious sect leader in front of her and touched a match to her gasoline-soaked clothes.

Her father, John R. Moore, executive vice-president of North American Aviation, called a press conference six days later, while Nancy lay in critical condition at the UCLA Medical Center with third-degree burns over 99% of her body, to "warn other young people about experimenting with the drug." Among other things, he said: "LSD brought on the tragic incident which has taken our beloved and once beautiful daughter, Nancy, charred and in agony, to death's door.

Nancy, an art student, had been using LSD for two years. Her father learned of it the day before she immolated herself. "She told me she didn't need him [a psychiatrist Nancy had been seeing] anymore," Moore said. "She told me she had the thing licked—whatever it was."

Nancy died August 1, 1966. Her apparent suicide caused headlines—headlines that others seem to ignore or drive from their minds.

A 19-year-old City College student in New York said that he took acid to "find some meaning in life." Jim, a San Francisco hippie, asserted: "LSD has taught me things about myself and my society that it would have taken me years to learn any other way." A coed at Hunter College, New York, said that LSD is popular "in the fraternities and with some of the people majoring in psych." A Brooklyn teenager claimed that LSD had helped him to remove some "emotional blocks."

Not all LSD users seek answers to hangups. Some are just curious or try it for kicks. "I'd heard so much about it. They said you could see the wonders of the world right in your own mind. I just figured I had to try it," admitted a 17-year-old high school student from Forest Hills, Queens.

Dr. Cohen, a prominent writer on the subject of LSD as well as a psychiatrist, has some clear-cut thoughts on the campus popularity of acid. Some excerpts from Cohen, as quoted in the 1966 Dell paperback *LSD on Campus* by Warren Young and Joseph Hixson are to the point: "On the magna-campus, where the faceless student goes through a sort of mill, the influence of the faculty is remote and the availability of the drugs is high. . . . There is a certain amount of social pressure to indulge. . . . We are an affluent society, so the kids can afford these drugs. . . ."

Then Cohen takes a slap at parents who give children everything: "If a young man has never been given direction or goals, if he hasn't been directed to achieve, then he gets to college fairly aimless, and one wonders whether the result won't be his seeking the magical, the easy and the painless, which is the pill way."

McGlothlin has effectively summed up other factors in the swing to the mind-swingers: "For young people, who are the most readily influenced by the drugs, the suspicion that the competition and concern for status in the adult achievement-oriented society is only a meaningless, materialistic rat race may be fortified by drugs. LSD seems to temporarily suspend the dominant system of values and allows other perspectives to come through."

Young acidheads are restless, rebellious and impatient in a world where old reliable standards are in a headlong rush to the scrap heap; Curiosity, kicks, social pressure, frustration, mental expansion, religious experience—whatever the excuse, the fact remains that too many youths are putting their minds on a sugary chopping block, unaware or unwilling to believe that LSD can lop them off into insanity without warning.

LSD's advocates scoffed at the danger signals raised by psychiatrists and they hailed the wonders of chemistry to such an extent that people in general were finally ready to accept acid as a boon to mankind. But little Donna's curiosity burst LSD's bubble and set off the crisis that has resulted in the facts on the true horror of the drug being brought to public attention.

The Tide Turns

THE OPENING of a refrigerator door brought to a screeching halt the steady climb of LSD to public acceptance as a key to unlocking mental mysteries.

On April 6, 1966, 5-year-old Donna Wingeroth awoke earlier than usual in the Brooklyn apartment shared by her divorced mother Linda, her uncle Paul Franklin and her grandmother Mrs. Anne Franklin. Feeling hungry, she went to the kitchen, opened the refrigerator, found a sugar cube and swallowed it. Within 20 minutes she began screaming and crying. Her cries alerted Paul who immediately noted that the LSD-impregnated sugar cube he had purchased was missing. Donna was rushed to Kings County Hospital, alternately screaming and silent. Doctors pumped her stomach and admitted her for observation.

Dr. Doris H. Milman, assistant professor of pediatrics at Downstate Medical Center, Brooklyn, reported on Donna's treatment in the September 1967 issue of the *Journal of the American Medical Association*. According to Dr. Milman, after Donna's initial fits of hysteria ended, she became temporarily psychotic and then suffered psychological after effects which lasted for nine months. For example, on that same day she experienced many "bizarre and apparently delusional ideas, such as the feeling that her body was cut off at the waist, that she was not herself but a girl named Dorothy, that it was not she but Dorothy who had eaten supper, and that she had gone home and her bed was occupied by a girl named Dorothy." In short, Donna became acutely psychotic with feelings of aggression, panic, depression which affected her intellectual functioning. On the next day she felt burning sensations and told of a dream in which "they stole my mommy and tried to cut me in half." Later, she reported that she saw angels and various animals.

These first evidences of disturbance vanished within a few days, but Donna's disoriented thinking continued for several months. Before that tragic morning, Donna had been a bright kindergarten pupil at Public School 206, with an I.Q. of 125. A day after the accident Donna's I.Q. measured 108, but four days after that it fell to 94. Five months later it was 121, and nine months later it returned to normal. Her brain waves, measured five months after the accident, were found to be still slightly abnormal, but this condition disappeared after nine months.

Donna's experience caused an uproar over LSD when it hit the newspapers. The story horrified parents who prior to that time had heard only good reports about the acid that some of their sons were trying on campus. The story also shook the psychedelic world preached by Leary, Alpert and acidheads, but for different reasons. They well realized that Donna's accident could spell trouble for their acid-based new society.

Then, on May 11, 1966, LSD was on the receiving end of another body blow. Stephen Kessler, a 30-year-old Harvard graduate with a "genius I.Q. of more than

170" and a former student at the Downstate Medical Center where Donna was hospitalized, snatched LSD from the worlds of science and religion, of the intellectual and the hip, and slammed it down in front of ordinary people who worry about their sons and daughters.

Mrs. Florence Cooper, a junior high school teacher whose Brooklyn apartment was a 15-minute drive from Donna's home, had telephoned her husband Isidore to tell him that their son-in-law was berating her because their 22-year-old daughter Miriam had left him after an argument. Isidore left work and hurried home. On entering the foyer, he found his wife's body. Her throat had been cut and she had been stabbed at least two dozen times in the chest, back, thigh and legs.

The police said that they found Kessler's face and hands covered with scratches and a bloody pile of clothes on the floor of his apartment. They reported Kessler told them: "Man, I've been flying for three days on LSD. Did I kill my wife? Did I rape anybody? What have I done?"

At his trial, Kessler, who admitted he had been on LSD for two years before the murder, testified that he took acid as part of his studies of psychoses. He swore that he did not remember whether he had killed his mother-in-law. On October 25, 1967, the jury acquitted Kessler by reason of temporary insanity, but ordered psychiatric tests to determine if he should be placed in a mental institution.

Public Reaction

The cases of Donna and Kessler were followed by a public outcry which had immediate repercussions.

The U.S. Food and Drug Administration used its powers to make the sale and distribution of LSD illegal. Early in 1968 Congress considered severe penalties for its possession, and scientists switched from probing possible beneficial uses of the drug to documenting its dangers. Meanwhile Sandoz had halted its domestic supplies of LSD. The firm, from its Hanover, New Jersey, offices, first cut off further supplies to all accredited researchers and then recalled what it had already sent them. The remaining quantities of acid were turned over to the National Institute of Health which issued a small quantity for selected controlled studies of the drug. At the same time, while hospital psychiatric wards reported increasing inflows of LSD victims, psychiatrists and biochemists began intensive investigations in an attempt to determine whether LSD was a nightmarish chemical that warped the mind, perhaps forever, and turned acidhead babies into freaks.

The Production of LSD

However, the acid advocates were fazed by all this activity, for they had already begun to produce the drug in their own pads. Although no one could devise the means for producing LSD without a sound chemistry background, almost anyone can make it with the help of the widely circulated, step-by-step, acid "cookbook." The process is not difficult and the materials needed are relatively cheap. All of the necessary equipment can be obtained for less than $100, and the vacuum pump, the most expensive single item, can be purchased for as little as $13.95. It takes four days to make LSD by the long method.

In its basic form, LSD is a powder-fine crystal. A

single dose, which is smaller than a grain of sugar, costs the dealer about five cents. The dealer can resell it for as much as $10.

Users who purchase acid illegally claim that they know how many micrograms they are getting. But one recent spot-check of street-sold LSD proved after chemical analysis, that in not one single case was an acidhead's estimate even close to the number of micrograms he actually received.

Blackmarket LSD cannot be carefully measured and subdivided by dealers. This is one of its great dangers. Most acid is kept in distilled water and stored in refrigerators. Each dose is measured with an eye dropper and fits handily on a sugar cube. Recently, because of the crackdown, a drop has been deposited on such items as postage stamps and allowed to dry. All it takes is one good lick for the user to mail himself to inner space.

The largest centers for the production of LSD are in and around San Francisco and Berkeley, California. But every large city has at least one clandestine laboratory to feed the market, and some of them are pretty cleverly camouflaged. On one occasion, a creamery truck was stopped on the Colorado border for passing a weighing station; the truck turned out to be a fully equipped rolling lab for making LSD, and it contained enough acid to bring its operators a $500,000 profit.

A tightly-knit network of friends distributes the bulk of acid used in this country. Only friends of the distributor (who is almost invariably a user himself) or those vouched for by friends can purchase acid. Most buy only enough from the dealer for themselves and a few confidants. The dealer himself is usually an acidhead who knows a source for obtaining quantities of LSD, normally an underground factory where the chemical is made. A dealer may have as many as 10,000 "trips" in his refrigerator.

United Press International reported on one network of friends that is typical of thousands of others flourishing across the country. Three hippie girls skipped down Haight-Ashbury Street, singing, "We're off to see the Wizard, the wonderful Wizard of Ows." Wizard, about 24 years old, was sitting at a coffee house table. He got his nickname because he distributes the product of an amateur chemist named Ows. The girls had a brief chat with him, but left without any acid. "This place is loaded with narcos [Federal Bureau of Narcotics agents]," Wizard said, and he told the girls that their LSD would be delivered later to their pad.

Imported LSD

A large quantity of LSD enters the United States in powder form from England, Italy (where it is made legally), Scandanavia, Switzerland, Czechoslovakia and Tangiers. College students, traveling in those places during their summer vacations, purchase LSD at bargain-basement prices and smuggle it back by methods so simple they are almost beautiful—until you figure out the number of freakouts that will result. For example, any customs agent knows that no self-respecting American would travel in Europe without his own, brought-from-home roll of soft toilet paper. But quite a few students have devised the scheme of unrolling a few yards of the paper, carefully placing the powder on a square and rerolling it completely with the outer wrapper neatly tucked in to prevent any loss.

One youth who used this system had 10,000 doses of LSD that he had purchased in London for $1,000 concealed in one roll of toilet paper. He dissolved the drug in just the right amount of distilled water and sold the batch for $20,000. Ballpoint pens with their refills removed, the pages of books and the bottom of cigarette packages are just a few more examples of the hundreds of ways—nearly impossible to detect—of smuggling LSD into the United States.

Dr. Sidney Cohen told a Senate committee in May, 1967 that during one European trip he was offered "a gram of LSD for $7,000. On that one gram—which is less than the size of a cigarette—I could have made $150,000 here." He also testified that the inevitable had happened—the criminal underworld had now become involved in the lucrative acid trade.

In June, 1967, John Finlater, chief of drug abuse control for the Food and Drug Administration, told the House Government Operations Subcommittee: "There is an extremely well organized traffic in hallucinatory drugs now functioning. The organization is affiliating with hard-core Cosa Nostra type criminal figures." Moreover, Finlater stated, mob-made LSD, in sharp contrast to the home-brew variety, is "practically quality-controlled" in tablet form. The illicit operations "employ physicists, chemists and other science professionals and equip large and sophisticated laboratories."

Detection of LSD use is difficult at best. There are no sure-fire tests to prove its presence in the body. A few outward signs can provide some indication that a person may be on acid, but they are hardly conclusive. For example, dilation of the pupils of the eyes is one sign, but it is one that also may be caused by other, quite legal drugs. (As a point of general interest, LSD may cause the pupils of an acidhead to become so dilated that he will protect himself against the light by wearing dark glasses even at night.) Other signs include difficulty in communication, the withdrawal from family and old friends, and the loss of interest in studies, hobbies, one's job and life in general, as well as a partial or complete change in personality. However, the trouble with these clues is that they are only red indicator lights. They can point to ensnarlment with chemicals of one form or another, but they can just as easily be the result of other factors.

Beneficial Aspects of LSD

The early popularity of LSD, in those innocent days before volunteer students discovered that they liked its effects, lay in the promise that it offered as some sort of wonder psychotherapeutic tool. After a great deal of extravagant praise, some tests were made to determine what beneficial results, if any, the use of acid might accomplish. In 1967 the National Institute of Mental Health spent $1.5 million on LSD research, $400,000 of that sum on six carefully controlled studies to discover if LSD was everything its adherents claimed it to be.

Researchers have probed acid's possibilities in helping alcoholics to quit drinking, in establishing rapport between therapist and patient, in treating autistic children and schizophrenic adults, in coping with sexual abnormalities and in easing the pain of terminal disease patients. Scientists have also conducted tests in the hope that LSD will produce model psychoses that will contribute to a clearer understanding of how the mind works.

Dr. Alpert discovered a somewhat different beneficial use of acid. He said that psychedelic drugs helped him to feel good when he watched his mother's funeral. He claimed that he felt beauty, not sadness. But Alpert aside, the basic idea behind the use of LSD as a mental tool is that it appears to break down a patient's defenses and lays bare his subconscious to the psychiatrist, a process which can take years on the couch. Doctors who have tested LSD in this regard claim that it helps patients to recall the traumatic experiences of their life, even back to early childhood, and to discuss them more freely. In their view, LSD allows patients to more easily overcome their natural reticence to speak openly, thus greatly speeding up the process of psychotherapy.

The Institute for Psychedelic Research, established in 1965 by scientists from San Francisco State College and Stanford University, is dedicated to the use of psychedelic agents "for bringing into conscious awareness aspects of mental processes which are usually unconscious or inaccessible." It reported that tests with 350 persons over several months resulted in "greater spontaneity of emotional expression and increasing self-confidence."

Dr. M. Robert Wilson, Jr., a Mayo Clinic psychiatrist, told a St. Louis seminar for science writers in the fall of 1967 that LSD uncovered and helped to rectify what he called a cause of considerable mental illness— the inability to express warmth to one's fellow man. He said that a test group of emotionally-disturbed adolescents had been given LSD as part of their treatment, and that a common underlying emotional effect had been achieved. One patient expressed it best when he said that during his trip he suddenly "felt free to be compassionate and warm." Evidence from the study indicates that at least some emotionally disturbed persons need "freedom to be warm and close." Wilson stressed, however, that LSD has potential psychological and physiological hazards. He made it clear that he was not condoning its use by anyone, except under controlled medical observation.

In the May 1966 *American Journal of Psychiatry,* Dr. James Simmons, chief of the Children's In-patient Service at the Neuropsychiatric Institute of UCLA, reported on LSD treatments given to a set of autistic, 5-year-old twins. He said that acid markedly reduced their mechanically rhythmic actions and their almost complete withdrawal from human contact.

Morphine and other opiates are used to ease the agonizing pain caused by cancer, but nothing had ever been discovered to alleviate the mental anguish that cancer and other fatal diseases cause. Dr. Eric Kast, research psychiatrist at the Chicago Medical School, used acid on 80 patients who knew that they would die within a few weeks. Kast reported at a conference at the University of California Medical Center, San Francisco, that the drug eased the patients' agony and even gave some "a new will to live."

Dr. Albert A. Kurland of the Maryland Department of Mental Hygiene had a similar experience. One of the members of his staff developed cancer and asked for LSD treatments. In May 1967, Kurland told a Chicago meeting of the American Medical Association that "she had definite relief from her anguish and an elevation of mood." During the same month, at a State

Health Department Conference in Buffalo, Dr. Henry
Brill, vice-chairman of the New York State Narcotics
Addiction Control Commission, disclosed the use of
LSD to relieve worries of terminal cancer patients in
state hospitals. He said that acid served to "control
normal anxiety—it relieves normal anxieties."

Much experimentation has been done in the hope
that LSD can aid in curing alcoholism. Dr. Ruth Fox,
prominent New York City psychiatrist and a leader in
this field, made a careful study of 20 chronic alcoholics.
The experiment began in December 1961 and lasted
until the following March. Her report, published in
The Use of LSD In Psychotherapy (Bobbs-Merrill,
1967), represented a three-year follow-up study of
those alcoholics.

Dr. Fox's subjects were intelligent people in the
middle- or upper-income brackets who had had success-
ful careers in diverse fields before being overcome by
drinking problems that had lasted as long as 35 years.
She reported that 16 of the 20 "severe, recalcitrant alcoholics" showed improvement with a "total push"
therapy, which, in addition to LSD, included group
therapy, affiliation with Alcoholics Anomymous, coun-
seling and other treatment.

Few of Dr. Fox's patients could say which part of
the therapy had helped them most. Most of the group,
she stated had "an unusual degree of motivation—a
vital factor in recovery." But she considered it significant that the changes in her LSD patients "were more
profound and more lasting than in the patients who did
not have this response. Harmful defenses can be broken
down and more appropriate ones can be developed. The

drug can certainly make the patient more open and receptive to future psychotherapy."

At the time of publication of her findings, Dr. Fox ceased the use of LSD on alcoholics. She told a reporter that while she stood by her report, acid has far too many dangerous side effects that far outweigh possible benefits.

Others have not had comparable success with LSD in the treatment of alcoholism. Psychologists Gerald Goldstein and William T. Bowen of the Veterans Administration Hospital, Topeka, Kansas, found little evidence that the drug aided drunkards, although about half of the 129 who were given acid went on the wagon for 90 days or more. However, Goldstein and Bowen achieved roughly the same results with a similar group treated without LSD.

The therapeutic claims made for LSD must be examined critically. "It is most unfortunate that at this time we do not know how helpful LSD might be, and we may never have the opportunity to discover, through appropriate research, how to channel this powerful chemical tool into productive clinical purposes because of its clouded future," Ungerleider and Fisher wrote in the July 1967 issue of *Medical Digest*. "Nonetheless, to summarize LSD's presently known therapeutic value, in the opinion of the authors, this must be considered unproven to date."

Dr. Jonathan Cole, who oversees the LSD studies for the National Institute of Mental Health, said that, hopefully, LSD will produce a schizophrenic model that could provide a key to mental illness, "but research on this has not been productive." Users may "get depressed or panicky or paranoid, but not much like in the case of real schizophrenia." One of his co-workers, Dr. Jerry Levine, put the hopes for chemical psychotherapy into greater perspective when he stated in the May 9, 1966 issue of the *National Observer* that although some "interesting leads" have developed, "definite conclusions cannot be drawn at this time."

What all this boils down to is that there are no miracles in acid's use. There is no evidence as of now that LSD is so dramatically effective that a couple of doses will relieve severe problems. In point of fact, those doses may cause severe injury, and while LSD loosens deep-buried problems, it does not reduce the amount of psychotherapy needed.

Crash Landings

THERE is no guarantee whatsoever against a bad ride on the acid express. Even veterans of a hundred rides through chemically contorted scenery have no assurance that the next one won't be shot through with hellish hallucinations. Under the most controlled circumstances—either clinical or under the close supervision of a hippie "guide"—acidheads have committed suicide or become so tormented that their minds were shattered. Extended hospitalization is often necessary after these flights to unsanity, and freakouts occur regardless of the source of the drug.

Bad Trips

Susan K. Abshear couldn't take her freakout. This 19-year-old University of California coed plunged, naked, through the closed, third-floor window of her Berkeley hippie district pad.

Clinical experiments with LSD are conducted with the utmost care. Volunteers are screened, and anyone who gives indications that he may panic or suffer extended bad reactions is weeded out. Once the volunteer has taken his dose of acid, psychiatrists watch his every reaction, and a medical doctor is present in case he is needed. Despite this care, however, a group of young physicians who volunteered to "fly" suffered some of the worst reactions seen by Ungerleider, while a controlled group of extremely disturbed, "marginal" types who claimed ingestion of large amounts of LSD showed "no discernible increase" in observable reaction.

Ungerleider and his associate, Fisher, in the July 1967 issue of *Medical Digest,* exploded two of the biggest myths peddled by acid advocates. One was the fiction that carefully screened, stable persons do not have freakouts. The other is the claim that LSD taken in the proper "setting" is safe. The doctors' report stated that experiences with over 70 carefully studied freakout cases showed that even psychological testing, psychiatric examination, the absence of symptoms and a history of stability will not ensure the user against a freakout.

Louria, who reviewed the records of more than 130 freakouts at Bellevue Hospital, stated in his book *Nightmare Drugs* (Pocket Books, Inc., 1966): "There can be no doubt that LSD can induce acute psychoses in an apparently healthy person." Louria went on to say that persons with personality instabilities or borderline psychos can take a swift turn toward acute psychoses with a push from LSD.

Dr. George J. Breitbart, a New York psychiatrist, writing in the June 1967 issue of *Glamour* magazine, likened the effect of LSD to a cracked pitcher that survives for years, its defect unnoticed, until it is nudged and smashes. LSD can take a minor defect that many persons carry through life without noticing it and turn that defect into an acute psychosis.

How can the very same drug which induces blissful nirvana provoke a terrifying psychosis? The answer is that the drug demolishes the defenses of the personality to cope with the stresses of life. A basically healthy person, relatively free of anxiety and hostility, can—but will not necessarily—have a good experience. But if the same defenses are shattered in an area of distrust or repressed conflicts, that person can go to pieces and stay that way.

Hippie folklore maintains that a clinic is the wrong place to test the reaction to LSD, inasmuch as it is considered to be cold, unfriendly and conducive to a bad trip. An acidhead must be calm. He is supposed to be in the company of good friends or an experienced "sitter" in a warm, familiar setting. The user must be comfortable, a state usually achieved by sitting on thick rugs or on a mattress. He is urged to listen to music, preferably of the Oriental variety, and to use a "trip book" to guide his mind through the fantasies of chemistry. And just in case anything goes wrong, he is advised to have a powerful tranquilizer handy.

This advice for chemical profit is put out by the very same acidheads who become the strongest opponents of LSD after just one bad experience. They have duped thousands into trips with glowing reports of the "consciousness expanding" possibilities of a voyage to inner space. Many of those who listened are now flowing into psychiatric emergency rooms with tangled, warped minds.

Increase in the Use of LSD

The New York State Council on Drug Addiction reported on February 27, 1967, that the use of LSD was on the rise, not only among college students, but also among the unstable, the neurotic, the borderline psychotic and the school dropout.

Many California state hospitals, Ungerleider reports, are admitting LSD victims with increasing frequency, and these patients, according to the hospitals, were normal before trying acid. They had not shown even the slightest sign of borderline emotional trouble before that time. Ungerleider and Fisher said they saw only about one freakout victim a month before September 1965. But since then the number has swelled to as many as 20 a month—victims who were actually seen, and not including those who phoned for help. This amounts to 12% of all the cases handled by the psychiatric emergency services.

Dr. William Frosch, psychiatrist at the New York University Medical Center, reported at a meeting of the American College of Neuropsychopharmacology in Puerto Rico on December 7, 1966, that an estimated 5% of admissions to Bellevue Psychiatric Hospital since December 1965 had at least one experience with LSD. A total of 20% of all patients, or more than 200, were taken in for crackups "directly resulting from ingestion of LSD." Brooklyn's Kings County Hospital Center, which is not widely known among hippies as a mecca for crash landings, reported in the July 1, 1967 issue of the *New York State Journal of Medicine* that 25 acidheads were treated in the psychiatric emergency room between August 15, 1965 and June 15, 1966. San Francisco's General Hospital, in the heart of hippiedom's national capital, sees more than 30 victims a week. The Haight-Ashbury Free Medical Clinic, founded by toxicologist David E. Smith, handles 20 or more cases each week.

These figures are far from complete. They encompass only a very few of the many state, city and private hospitals that admit freakouts. And many more crackup cases, whether because of fear or because fellow acid-heads have advised them to stay away, never appear,

Many of the victims who turn up at these psychiatric emergency rooms claim that LSD overdoses are responsible for their reactions of fear, panic and psychosis. A normal LSD dose is up to 250 micrograms of the drug. Most users have no idea how much acid they are getting. Ungerleider and Fisher report seeing freakouts among persons who have had as little as 100 micrograms, whereas some persons who have taken 2,000 micrograms daily for weeks have suffered not the slightest adverse reaction. Tolerance for LSD develops rapidly with repeated daily doses and vanishes completely three days after the last ingestion. But most users, aware of acid's strong effects, take it about once a month, using marijuana to fill in between trips.

Mental Effects of LSD

Hippies, whether hard-core, weekenders or plastic types who drop out occasionally, take acid for a variety of reasons. Some do it for kicks, others for religious experiences, or to improve their personalities, consciousness, sexual potency, artistic potential, etc. There are scores of reasons that users give for shoving their heads into the acid bag. But the bag is bursting. Evidence is growing that acid may kick users' minds out of whack. Donna and Kessler first alerted the nation, and since then numerous studies have probed the mental effects of LSD. Three important reports have already been issued—the first by Ungerleider and Fisher, then one by Frosch and, more recently, one by Michael Blumenfield and Lewis Glickman of Kings County Medical Center.

Ungerleider and Fisher's study appeared in the August 1966 *Journal of the American Medical Association.* It discussed 70 freakout cases, but focused on 25 of that number who required hospitalization—19 of them for more than a month and some for as long as five months. The great majority of the 70 who sought care between September 1965 and April 1966 were young, white males. Most of them were non-religious and most used marijuana in addition to acid. Some had taken only a single trip, while others had had as many as 60 before that one bad flight brought them to UCLA. Twenty of them had not taken acid in six weeks, and fully half had abstained at least a week before seeking help. Most boarded their flights in the so-called proper settings and with experienced hosts on hand.

The Bellevue study by Frosch, who was assisted by Dr. Edwin Robbins and Dr. Marvin Stern, was based on three samples taken from the large number of acidheads admitted. A total of 57 were probed: the first 12 admitted early in 1965, the first 22 admitted in 1966, and 23 who were admitted late in 1966. Of the 57, 93% were white, 91% were unmarried (mainly because they were too young or students), and 56% were male. They ranged in age from 15 to 43, but had a median age of 22.

The first two samples included only those admitted as a direct result of LSD. The last group included all those in Bellevue at the time who had taken acid. Of the 57, 54% had taken less than five flights, 12% up to 10 trips, 16% up to 30 and 18% up to 100. Most of them also used marijuana.

All but one of the first group of 12 were in their twenties. Most had some college education, but only two were graduates. Most were deeply interested in philosophy and Eastern religions. All had some personality defect before taking LSD. Of those first 12, four had taken acid alone at home. Another two had been brought in by friends who had apparently failed in their attempts to control the trip. A seventh had fallen from a window while assisting a novice on his first experience. Two of the seven were classed as schizophrenics and three others as borderline cases. The remaining two had personality disorders.

One-third of the LSD victims in the Frosch-Bellevue report had prolonged reactions to acid, including states of chronic anxiety and chronic psychoses. They suffered from visual phenomena, depersonalization and body image distortions—characteristics deceptively identical to those exhibited by schizophrenics. Chronic anxiety states were common and often accompanied by depression and difficulty in functioning while remaining in contact with surroundings. The condition would last for months and resist treatment by medication or psychotherapy.

Three of the patients who suffered psychotic states, Frosch said, were not believed to be psychotic before they took LSD. They claimed that they took LSD in the belief that it would increase their self-understanding. While under LSD, the three believed that they had had experiences of greater personal significance than any they had known previously. As acid gripped their brains, they believed they had solved their hangups and created a new self. However, they suffered crash landings as the effects of the drug wore off. They had to return to the real world and to accommodate themselves to it. Conflict arose as their new understanding was not understood or responded to by others. They strove to maintain their "new world" and withdrew from the old.

The 25 subjects of the report by Dr. Blumenfield and Dr. Glickman ranged in age from 18 to 30, with an average age of 22. Almost three-quarters of this group were male. According to their claimed religious affiliation, there were 12 Catholics, 7 Jews, 5 Protestants and one whose faith was unknown. At least 18 of the 25 had had previous psychiatric help before trying LSD. Within the group, 20% had taken acid once, 60% up to 10 times and 20% more than that. Fifteen of them were classed as schizophrenics and five as borderline cases.

The most significant aspect of the Blumenfield-Glickman report is its figures that show the use of LSD to be spreading to a lower socio-economic group. Acid had previously been confined almost exclusively to the educated, white middle class. But as opposed to the UCLA and Bellevue studies, only 80% of the Kings County group were white. Fully 56% of the group did not complete high school and 26% were unemployed. The average school grade finished was below the 11th. Many of the dropouts had histories of anti-social behavior and criminal offenses, as well as previous drug experiences, including heroin.

The above figures give a statistical portrait of these three important reports that will be cited throughout this chapter as we probe the almost unnerving findings of LSD's action on the mind. It must also be remembered that hospitalized freakouts represent but a few of the total who have crash-landed. Some of the less fortunate wound up in morgues, like 22-year-old Roy Buell.

Roy was determined to find himself. Shortly before Thanksgiving in 1966 he admitted to his mother that he had been using LSD for six months, and he cried: "I've blown my mind." Then, promising her that it would never happen again, Roy loaded his car with camping gear and drove south from San Francisco in search of himself in the solitude of the outdoors. His body and his .22 calibre pistol were found in April 1967 by Mexican officials on the beach near Ensenada in Baja, California. A bullet had passed through his head. "It was suicide," his mother told a press conference designed to warn others of the dangers of using LSD.

The Victims of LSD

In a hospital, acute reaction to LSD is treated by providing an environment of comforting support and reassurance from a nurse or attendant who also restrains the freakout from harming himself. Strong tranquilizers help to counter acid's effects, but not in all cases. An attending psychiatrist also tries to reassure the victim that LSD's effects will wear off and that he will return to normal. The acidhead is urged to relax and to flow with the acid. Strenuous efforts to overcome the effects of acid only serve to increase distortions, confusion and panic.

The majority of freakouts taken into psychiatric emergency rooms are suffering acute reactions to their chemical voyage. They seek admittance while suffering hallucinations, extreme anxiety, confusion and depression. Frosch reported that one 21-year-old girl was convinced of the power of LSD to help break down her sexual hesitation that so angered her lover. But shortly after she took a dose, she saw the bricks in a wall moving in and out. She became frightened, unable to tell her body from the chair she was sitting on or from the body of her lover. When the lover brought her to Bellevue, she was laughing hysterically, joining others who were crying, screaming and moaning.

Panic reactions brought in 53% of the 57 in the Frosch-Bellevue study. Another 33% came in after experiencing continued reactions to acid long after they stopped taking the drug. A further 33% sought help because of prolonged reactions. At Kings County, four of the 25 admitted tried suicide after panic set in, three of them by slashing their wrists. Two more attempted murder, while another tried to wreck his parents' home. Still another made a sexual advance on a 5-year-old boy on the street.

Under the direct action of LSD on the brain, the user, in response to delusions of power or persecution, may expose himself to death, as 32-year-old Robert Tupy did. Tupy was a legend in San Francisco. "In order to be indestructible, you have to believe that you are indestructible," he would tell fellow hippies. After dropping out with LSD, Tupy would walk across busy streets against traffic lights, and once he rode his motor scooter into a parked car, walking away without so much as a scratch. Then, to prove his power, he stepped in front of a moving freight train. There wasn't much left of Tupy but the now discredited legend.

Panic victims frequently fear they are going crazy—and, in fact, some do. They have a sense of helplessness and a loss of control, and are often afraid that they will never return to normal. At Hermosa Beach, near Los Angeles, four teenagers rammed their car into a house, killing a 3-year-old child. According to police the driver was in an "LSD trance" and kept trying to climb the wall of his jail cell, yelling: "I'm a Graham Cracker—oops, my arm crumbled off."

The Frosch-Bellevue study, going further, said that a user may be unable to cope with seemingly conflicting material presented while under LSD's influence. He cited the case of a man who took acid shortly after his wife died and felt an unrealistic guilt about her death. This man, who ended up slashing his wrists, also experienced flashbacks to traumatic memories of his earlier life.

Does LSD Truly Expand Consciousness?

Acid buffs claim benefits of greater selfunderstanding, heightened perception, increased creative powers, extra closeness to God and new love for fellow men. Poet Allen Ginsberg maintains that LSD helped to clear his consciousness and make possible some of his best works.

Do acidheads actually profit from the school of chemistry or do they only feel they have? If they profit, few if any of these improvements are obvious to the square society. In fact, hippie behavior points to the opposite view, the one taken by psychiatrists. An examination of these claims, point by point, bears out the conclusion that acid actually retards improvement.

According to the acid test, a simple prod from LSD

can make petals of flowers seem alive with vibrant life, and they claim that acid helps perception in general, especially the vibrations emitted by humans. However, Ungerleider and Fisher closely examined the members of one group who claimed that their perception was rocketed into orbit with an acid booster. They found that "their ability to discriminate was below normal, and that their powers of observation had been decreased." Even hippiedom's own doctor, David E. Smith, has reported that most of those who come into the Free Clinic complain of perception problems. "They see rings around lights or have trouble 'spacing.'" Some, he said, ask if their brains have been damaged.

LSD causes delusions and the loss of time sense. Users have been known to stare at parts of their bodies or at flowers or at almost any object for hours on end. Some have stared at the sun until they were blinded forever. According to Ungerleider, one acidhead was convinced that he had to offer human sacrifice, and he attempted to throw his girlfriend from a hotel roof.

Dr. Sidney Malitz, chief of psychiatric service at Columbia University's Psychiatric Institute, described LSD's greatly ballyhooed "consciousness-expanding" powers in these terms: "It's like a dream when you think you have the answer to some problem, but when you wake up the answer just doesn't stand up." But it remained for Ungerleider to give the coup de grace to the consciousness-expanding hokum when he wrote: "LSD has been called a 'consciousness-expanding' drug while it is, in fact, quite the reverse. The drug *decreases* one's ability to select and pay attention; thus it decreases conscious functions. Sensations do become intensified following LSD. Perception, however, is *not*

enhanced and visual, auditory acuity and general awareness are *not* 'revolutionized' but rather distorted."

Huxley contended that LSD enhances creativity, and
Leary, his disciples and hippiedom in general raise this
claim first when asked what acid does for them. But, as
one psychiatrist stated at a University of Maryland
panel discussion in May, 1966: "Huxley's creative work
was 1% mescaline and 99% Huxley." The same could
be said of Ginsberg and his poetry. Another speaker,
Dr. William Murphy, a psychoanalyst, said that LSD is
actually dangerous to creative people because it can
slow their drive. Moreover, Murphy claimed, it is also
bad for the uncreative because they get the subjective
idea that they are creative.

McGlothlin administered a variety of psychological
tests to 24 volunteers two weeks before, two weeks after
and six months after they had taken LSD. He found
no increase in creativity or aesthetic sensitivity but did
find increased passivity and introspective attitudes. As
for Cohen, he states flatly that "artistic inspiration can
only be executed by one who has already mastered the
technique of the medium." He considers that drive is
also necessary for creativity, and LSD "will reduce
motivation as often as it will intensify it."

Effects of LSD on Personality

LSD has a striking effect on personality. The advocates of chemical togetherness claim that under the influence of LSD they are more tender and loving toward
others, even their enemies. A favorite way for cartoon-
ists to depict hippies is to draw them showering an
arresting police officer with flowers.

Ungerleider and Fisher visited several community

dances where the flower children gathered. Beneath undulating psychedelic colors, they observed long-haired boys dancing with barefoot girls in slacks and reported that LSD seemed to replace personal contact and substitute for sexual drive and aggression. "There was little male-female awareness or physical contact; each was in his own fantasy world." They then concluded: "In contradiction to the claim that the drug helps one to get closer to people, we note that users become more introspective and invested in themselves. The extreme results are autism and psychoses."

Ungerleider also reported on a hippie "love-in" he attended: "Everybody was talking about love in grand general terms, but each one was actually having his own monologue, unaware that there was anyone else around. They became so invested in themselves and their intra-psychic processes that they couldn't reach out to other people."

Frosch said that his Bellevue patients showed no evidence of personality changes for the better. In three users he found a deterioration of personality following acid trips. Such deterioration, he said, became most noticeable under stress. Instead of mobilizing to counter anxiety, the patients became depersonalized and had a return of chemically-inspired hallucinations. And Louria has observed that LSD might permanently alter the personality structure of the individual. Furthermore, he considers it possible that the potency of the drug may mean that only a single dose would be necessary to cause a permanent change.

LSD drives the user into himself. Rather than enhancing the social nature of human beings, it drives acidheads inward. They become intensely interested in self. The difference between the acidhead swirling in his own chemically-built world and mental patients may be only one of degree—or time.

LSD-induced behavior patterns are remarkable in their similarity to those caused by schizophrenia, a serious mental disease which involves loss of contact with the environment and disintegration of the personality. This similarity was one of the initial sparks that set off early research into the drugs' possible beneficial uses.

A distraught Los Angeles mother was a horrified eye-witness to the pattern at work. She told newsmen in early 1967 what led to the confinement of her 19-year-old son in a state mental institution. He had taken his first dose of LSD by injection in February. In March, he was afflicted with serum hepatitis, apparently caused by an infected needle. While the youth's mother, a registered nurse, cared for him at home, "one of his friends slipped him some LSD." Realizing that something was wrong, she decided to sleep on a couch near her son. "I woke up and found him completely covered with blood. There was blood all over the floor. I saw a razor blade and realized what had happened. He had slit his arm inside the elbow."

The youth was taken to UCLA's medical center where the wound was treated. On regaining consciousness, the boy asked his mother: "Why didn't you sleep another hour and let me die?" Fearing another suicide try, she had her son transferred to the psychiatric unit of the county hospital. While there, he broke a glass and ripped his other arm and his throat. Later, he took a pencil and tried to stab himself. Two orderlies grabbed him, but he broke loose and tried to ram his head against a wall. Then he tried to poke his eyes out with his fingers.

Mental health counselor Mark D. Sanders interviewed the youth after he was strapped to a bed. "When asked with whom he lived, he said he lived with God. He did not know how old he was, and when I asked when he was born, he stated that he was not born, he had been created." Then he told Sanders: "When I see my face in the mirror, I see it turn into a thousand faces."

Distortion of a Sense of Values

Acid, after only a few trips, can and frequently does demolish its users' value systems. Dr. Sidney Malitz, chief of psychiatric research at the New York State Psychiatric Institute, has stated that psychic habituation occurs in certain users who will seek out more acid and gradually center their lives around LSD and its psychedelic possibilities, to the neglect of their careers, families, friends and everything else. Frosch noted that many of his patients felt a loss of ambition, often accompanied by the idea that life is a game, with withdrawal from competition and social interaction as the result.

To adolescents, struggling to establish their identities, LSD can be a panacea for aggression and sexuality by denying both feelings. After the opening gambits of hippie conversation and psychedelic clothing, teenagers plunge into the experience, and it sucks them in until, as Ungerleider stated, their search for identity becomes "a florid psychotic nightmare." He then added: "There is perhaps no period of life more loaded with conflict, and one might therefore expect that adolescents who took LSD would experience severe complications, including panic states, prolonged psychoses and severe depressions. This is the single greatest tragedy to accrue to LSD."

Another factor in the horror of LSD is its recurring effects. Acid symptoms—including panic, severe anxiety, hallucinations, confusion, severe depression and suicidal wishes—continue long after the drug has vanished from the body, and these symptoms are particularly prevalent in times of stress.

Fisher, in a March 30, 1967 *New York Times* interview, said that these recurring effects may strike not only habitual users but also those who have had only a single trip. And, according to Ungerleider, acid action "can occur for one year after the drug has been taken in all [its] intensity, whether there is stress or no stress."

Reports on the devasting mental effects of LSD are still coming in. The layman who doesn't subscribe to medical journals will read about them in newspaper accounts with increasing frequency—perhaps side by side with a horrifying story about the latest freakout. And as if the mind-warping effects of LSD were not enough, reports are now coming in on the genetic effects of the drug on the chromosomes and the resultant likelihood of malformed children.

Fly Now,
Pay Later

UNTIL recently, the juries who have been handing down indictments against LSD have been composed almost exclusively of psychiatrists. However, in the March 17, 1967 issue of *Science,* the weekly journal of the American Association for the Advancement of Science, a scientist at the State University School of Medicine, Buffalo, N.Y., disclosed the first evidence of biochemical damage.

Biochemical Damage

Dr. Maimon M. Cohen's analysis of the blood of LSD users revealed bent, misshapen and irregular chromosomes. Chromosomes are the microscopic, rod-like structures inside the nucleus of a cell; they are composed of long strands of deoxyribonucleic acid (DNA), the substance which controls all heredity. Each human cell has 46 chromosomes, and each chromosome has thousands of genes, the "genetic code" or key to heredity. The genes direct the specific activity of each cell.

Cohen set out to show that acid not only rearranges the mind but can cause biochemical damage. In two tests, conducted simultaneously, he found evidence that

LSD wreaks havoc among the chromosomes. In the first test, he placed normal white cells from three men and three women in test tubes. After dissolving LSD in sterile water and adding it, in varying small amounts, to the cells, he discovered "a marked increase" in the frequency in which the chromosomes broke and then reunited into different forms when compared to untreated blood.

Next, Cohen examined blood cells taken from a mental patient who had been treated with 15 doses of LSD over a period of more than five years. The 51-year-old man had also been treated for short periods of time with two tranquilizing drugs in conjunction with psychotherapy for paranoid schizophrenia. Cohen's screening of chromosomes from 35 other schizophrenics revealed no increase in breaks over that found in individuals who had not been treated with tranquilizers. But the man treated with LSD had chromosome breaks three times that of a normal person, and damage found in his cells more than six months after his last LSD treatment suggested residual damage.

Just a few months after Cohen's report was published, Dr. Jose Egozcue, a geneticist at the University of Oregon, addressed an American Psychiatric Association meeting in Detroit to report on the results of his work—results which supported the Buffalo findings. He found an unusually high incidence of genetic damage in six of the eight LSD users studied. In sharp contrast, he found genetic damage in only one of the nine members of a controlled group who had never taken LSD—and the one who did have damage had previously undergone extensive X-ray treatments, often known to cause such damage. Moreover, a later study of 18 LSD users by Cohen, in collaboration with Dr. Kurt Hirschorn of Mount Sinai Hospital, New York City, showed that the blood cells of nearly all were damaged.

The Children of LSD Users

A year after he raised the specter of chromosomal damage, Cohen told a national conference on psychedelic drugs sponsored by the Illinois State Medical Society in Chicago that men or women who take LSD may be jeopardizing their own lives as well as those of their future children. Cohen based his conclusions on a study which had shown that eight of 12 children born to admitted LSD users also had chromosomal damage. The LSD had been taken in the early months of pregnancy. Stating his belief that "the production of congenital defects is therefore a distinct possibility in this group," Cohen also reported that a study of 220 acid users had revealed that between 70% and 80% had chromosomal damage. This is four times the normal rate. In addition, he told of experiments with rodents which indicated that LSD alters the chromosomal structure of both the female egg and male sperm cells.

On September 6, 1967 the National Foundation of the March of Dimes brought together a panel of nine experts—including Cohen, an associate professor of pediatrics, obstetricians, geneticists and biologists—to discuss the genetic hazards of LSD to the user and his children. The panel warned that no one in his reproductive years—that is, from the teenage years to advanced middle age—should take acid unless there was a very good medical reason for doing so. Moreover, it stated that in its opinion there was no good medical reason for doing so.

The first documented case of a child who was born deformed after its mother had taken LSD during early pregnancy was confirmed by a pediatrics professor at the State University of Iowa on November 24, 1967. Dr. Hans Zellweger said that the woman, a 19-year-old Iowa resident who took acid on four occasions during the seventh week of pregnancy, gave birth to a baby girl with a deformed right leg. The malformation was similar to that found in babies during the thalidomide drug episodes of the early 1960's. According to Zellweger, studies of thalidomide babies showed that infants were born deformed when the drug was taken during the seventh week of pregnancy. The Iowa girl had taken LSD—and no other drug—during her seventh week. All structures of her baby's right leg were shorter than those of the left leg. The right foot had but three toes and was smaller than the left, and the right leg was attached to the torso at the hip at an odd angle. In Zellweger's opinion, the defects were apparently caused by a chromosomological breakdown in the mother that was transferred to the child.

It may take two or three generations before the final verdict is in, but as of now the evidence points to the conclusion that an LSD flight now may result in deformed children or grandchildren later.

Results of LSD Tests on Animals

Experiments on animals do not necessarily indicate what will happen to humans, but LSD has been given to animals as a standard drug-testing method. Two series of tests in particular have attracted wide notice. One was performed on hamsters at the Medical College of Georgia and reported in the October 1967 issue of *Science* by Dr. William F. Geber Jr., an associate professor of pharmacology. The other was performed on rats by George J. Alexander, Sandra Machiz and Rita B. Alexander, members of the medical research staff at the New York State Psychiatric Institute. Their findings were presented on April 16, 1968 at a meeting in Atlantic City of the Federation of American Societies for Experimental Biology.

In the Geber tests, hamsters were given injections of LSD, mescaline and brom-lysergic acid on the 8th day of pregnancy. The fetuses, examined on the 12th day, showed malformations of the brain, spinal cord, liver and other organs. Geber concluded that both LSD and its BOL derivative "are capable of inducing a wide variety of congenital malformations in the hamster embryo." He warned that the drugs should not be taken except under medical supervision.

The other report, entitled "Inherited Abnormalities in Three Generations of Offspring of LSD-Treated Rats," said that when LSD was administered either orally or by injection to hundreds of rats early in pregnancy, it resulted in "damage to litters that was three to four times higher" than in rats who had been given distilled water in a saline solution. The damage of offspring persisted into the second and third generations and was significantly higher when both parents were themselves offspring of LSD-affected mothers. The report concluded: "We would recommend . . . extreme caution in the use of LSD, whether for therapeutic or hedonistic reasons, at least until more data are obtained, because of the possibility of hidden or delayed damage."

We have examined the important known facts about LSD. Several conclusions are obvious: the drug is immensely powerful, its reactions are unpredictable, it is a threat to the mental and physical health of its users, and it is readily available to those who seek it. But the reader must draw his own conclusions, based on the facts presented here and on other reports he may read. He is the one who must decide whether the alleged promise of LSD is worth blowing his mind—perhaps for life—and gambling not only with his own health and well-being but also with that of his children and the generations that are to follow.

Marijuana:
Fact and Fiction

T HE WIDESPREAD use of marijuana today has bred a wealth of misinformation. Parents, educators and law officers preach endlessly about pot's supposed horrors, but today's informed youth knows the score. They want fact, not fantasy, truth, not lies.

Lies, Myths and Distortions

So many myths about marijuana, the "killer weed," have been spread that youth no longer listens. Therefore, the most blatant fables need to be discarded here and now, before we can have any reasonable discussion about the Mexican hemp that more than 20 million Americans have sampled at least once.

First, marijuana is not addictive. Its use will not lead to the heroin needle. It is true that over 80% of heroin users started on pot, but their total number, nationwide, is minute compared to the millions who have puffed pot. Nor will marijuana open the door to LSD use. Pot is not, as its strangest opponents charge, a menace that leads to violent crime. And, despite popular belief, it does not spur sexual drive, but actually diminishes it! As Bruce Jackson, a Harvard fellow who did a drug study for the President's Crime Commission, stated: "One of the reasons so many youngsters are taking drugs is that they have discovered this is one of these areas the older generation has made it a point to lie about."

Jackson's point is that when many young people sneak a puff of pot despite parental warnings and suffer none of the predicted disastrous consequences, they reason that if their parents were so wrong about marijuana, they could also be wrong about amphetamines, barbiturates and heroin. This parental credibility gap is the very same one that led so many young people to mental torment and unwitting trouble before the revolution that swept the once hush-hush topic of sex out into the open and led to proper educational programs at home and in school. And just such a revolution is needed to educate youth about marijuana which, although the mildest of the hallucinogenic substances, is not an entirely innocent social diversion without any psychic significance.

That attitudes are changing toward marijuana— once the "tea" of the Negro slum dwellers and a jazz musicians and beatnik set—is evident from an Associated Press survey of its use in several New England colleges. "When you went to a fraternity party at the University of Massachusetts last year, they offered you a drink," one student told an interviewer. "The student who cares about himself is smoking marijuana now."

Marijuana has become a white, middle-class thing today, and those who believe its use is confined to hippies are either blind, deaf or 98 years old. It's found in the schools, at parties and in the very best of homes. And no youth today, no matter how "innocent" or "protected," is without a source for pot. All it takes is an ounce of social pressure to convince him to try it, and if he doesn't know where to buy it himself, he knows someone who knows someone. Therefore, it is almost mandatory that young people be given the true facts about marijuana. In this way—and only in this way—can they be protected.

The Facts about Marijuana

Just what is this marijuana we're talking about? A good, hard look is necessary before exploring what damage it does or does not do. Although federal officials estimate that anywhere from 300,000 to 4,500,000 Americans puff pot regularly, severe penalties against its sale or possession make an accurate count nearly impossible. What is known, however, is that the U.S. Customs people seized 26,313 pounds of marijuana during the year that ended June 30, 1967. This was fully twice the amount seized in 1966, but it still represents only a very tiny fraction of the amount of weed available from home-grown and imported sources.

Marijuana is but one product of a tall and ancient female plant that was first described in a book on pharmacy by Chinese Emperor Shen Nung in 2737 B.C. Shen called it a "liberator" of sin, but he used it as a pain killer. About 800 B.C. it was introduced to India, and it spread from there to North Africa where the Crusaders found it in the 12th century. It reached Europe about 1800. Linnaeus gave the ugly plant the name *Cannabis sativa* in 1753.

Marijuana has long been used in Mexico and elsewhere south of the border. Mexican laborers brought their hemp into the United States around 1910 for use as a relaxant on the job. Its use greatly increased with the start of Prohibition after World War I, and during the depression of the 1930's the need to escape the harsh reality of the moment became nearly compulsive. As movie theaters boomed, pot crept across the South to the jazz musicians of New Orleans and then leapt into popularity in the Eastern urban slums.

The male hemp plant, a cousin of the fig tree and the stinging nettle, is used only to make rope. But the female, as it basks in the hot summer sun, produces a sticky, alkaloidal, oozing substance with a minty fragrance which seeps down from the yellow flower clusters above its seven-lobed leaves. This substance is a resin containing tetrahydro cannabinol, marijuana's active ingredient. Its extremely complex chemistry is not fully understood, although at long last a number of studies are now under way.

The strength of the experience that the female hemp plant induces varies considerably, depending on what part of the plant is used and, to some extent, where the hemp was grown. The nearly pure resin of the plant, dried into brownish-grey blocks, is most popular in India. Known as charas, it is by far the most potent product of the hemp plant. Hashish, most popular in the Middle East and used with increasing popularity in the United States, is a powdered and sifted form of charas. Both charas and hashish are usually smoked. Ganja, used mostly in India, consists only of the plant's flowering tops which are cut, dried, pulverized and smoked. It is also mixed into sweet desserts and tea. Bhang, again used mainly in India, is low in potency and is usually taken as a drink. Preparations roughly equal to bhang are smoked under the name of kief in North Africa, dagga in South Africa and marijuana in

Latin America, Europe and the United States.

One reason for the variety of stories about the effects of marijuana are these very differences in the power of the various hemp preparations. An opponent of the drug will quote Eastern material, while an advocate will be more inclined to cite Western findings. One favorite argument for condemning its use centers on violence and dates back to an 11th-century North African band, properly named the Assassins, whose leader would hop them up on the more potent forms of hemp and then send them off to do their dirty work!

About 95% of the hemp used in the United States comes in a steady, heavy flow from Mexico. Bearing the Mexican Spanish name for Mary Jane (marijuana), it consists of the flowers, leaves and stems of the hemp which are cut, dried, compacted and crumbled. Mc-Glothlin rates marijuana only one-fifth to one-eighth as potent as charas or hashish, principally because of the flowers, leaves and stems—and even seeds—that lessen its resin content.

The misnomen hashish comes from the year 1090 when a Moslem, Hasan-i-Sabah, used it in his fortress near Baghdad to pep up his soldiers. Christians of the first Crusade returned to Europe with the name, using it to denote hemp. To this day hashish carries the connotation of violence because Hasan-i-Sabah's soldiers would murder without hesitation while under the drug's influence.

There is wide variety in the quality of marijuana—and therefore in the experience of smoking it—depending on climate and cultivation. Acapulco Gold—recently the title and subject of a pop record—tops the scale. It is grown near the Mexican city of that name, and because it is more resinous, it is considered the vintage hemp, costing about twice as much as the more common varieties. Panama Red, supposedly from that Central American nation, is another prime cut and far more powerful than the mangy windowbox variety grown by economical hippies in New York's East Village or the Manhattan Silver found in that city's sewers—the result of evidence being flushed away hastily during police raids.

Marijuana can be grown anywhere in the United States. Recently, detailed mimeographed maps were circulated through the hippie pads of the East Village showing the exact locations of pot plantations throughout the state of Iowa. Needless to say, a copy of the map fell into the hands of state troopers who did most of the harvesting.

Incidental Facts

Only a small proportion of those who use marijuana smoke it regularly. Most users smoke about one cigarette a day, but the potheads may consume anywhere from six to ten daily. The price of a marijuana cigarette varies with the distance from the source of supply. In California, the land of plentiful pot, puggy "joints" can be purchased for as little as 25 cents each, while New Yorkers have to pay five dollars for three anemic "sticks." Those who can raise the price chip in as much as $200 for pound lots. The price rises and falls depending not only on the crop, quality and distance but also on police pressure.

California potheads toss away the butts of marijuana cigarettes, but New Yorkers prize these butts, known as roaches. True potheads believe that the potency of hemp is greatest in the last third of the cigarette and produces a far more intense effect. The marijuana underground has even solved the problem of how to hold roaches. No Bowery toothpicks for them! Special roach holders, some of them jeweled, can be purchased in hippie shops.

The variety in smoking methods is almost infinite. A marijuana "cocktail" is a non-filter cigarette with half of its tobacco replaced by pot. Some marijuana smokers swear by pipes because in that way they don't waste a shred of pot. Others prefer water pipes for that cool smoke.

Smoking marijuana is a roll-it-yourself deal, and there are dozens of cigarette papers available, including Marfil from Spain, Rizza Plus from France and Tip Top from America's own Liggett and Meyers. Most popular are the licorice-flavored Stella from England, Bambu from Spain and Zig-Zag, which comes in wheat straw or regular white paper. Pot is sprinkled into the cigarette paper and rolled very thinly to prevent any loss of the precious smoke to outside air. The papers are pre-creased and have gummed edges for sealing. Once rolled, the ends are tightly twisted to save every scrap of pot until light-up time.

The frills of marijuana smoking attest to its wide-spread use. Pop records sing its praises, while the smiling, bearded smoker on the back of the Zig-Zag pack has become a symbol used on buttons and sweatshirts that advocate legalization of pot. However, this is not a new story. Marijuana lit up newspaper headlines in the 1930's. Lurid New York stories of Harlem "tea pads" shocked the public. While women wept and laughed and adored moppet Shirley Temple and men looked with longing at Jean Harlow in movie house escape chambers, slum dwellers forgot their miseries in a cloud of pot.

More and more the press linked marijuana to the goriest murders, most perverted rapes and bloodiest assaults. New Orleans added fuel to the fire and fanned the public outcry by estimating that over 50% of that city's most ghastly crimes were marijuana-inspired. Newspapers stated that pot led to total insanity, sex orgies and violent crime, and frustrated Prohibitionist Henry J. Anslinger and his Federal Bureau of Narcotics backed a great "marijuana menace" campaign. Anslinger further fanned the flames, charging at one congressional hearing that a single "reefer" could conceivably make a man homicidal, turning him into a maniac who would slay his own brother. He even told a House subcommittee that birds who ate seeds of the hemp plant would stop singing!

Laws concerning Marijuana

Congress reacted and in 1937 passed the Marijuana Tax Act, setting harsh penalties for selling or even possessing marijuana. Today, marijuana offenders are subject to the provisions of the Narcotic Control Act of 1956 which amended the 1937 law as well as the Harrison Act of 1914 (which was the basic law against opiates). The 1956 law prescribed mandatory minimum sentences with no possibility of probation or parole for peddlers and smugglers of drugs. Illegal sale by a first offender was made punishable by a prison sentence of 5 to 20 years and a possible fine up to $20,000. Subsequent offenses were subject to a prison term of 10 to 40 years plus a fine up to $20,000. Possession was made punishable by imprisonment of 2 to 10 years for a first offense, 5 to 20 years for a second offense and 10 to 20 years for subsequent offenses, plus the discretionary $20,000 fine. The law was amended in 1966 to allow the parole of a marijuana offender—user or seller— after completion of one-third of his sentence; a suspended sentence or probation was authorized for first offenders convicted of possession. The amendment also allowed voluntary commitment of addicted persons to medical institutions, instead of prison, for long-term treatment. This was designed particularly to deal with heroin addicts.

Some states have harsher laws covering marijuana. It would be impossible to list all the variations here, but in 1968 New York, to cite just one example, made it possible for a seller of marijuana to be sentenced to life imprisonment. This law was passed on the theory that if the sellers were cut down, the flow of pot would be stemmed.

However, laws have failed to stem the popularity of pot. GI's by the thousands used it during World War II, Korea and Vietnam. In the 1950's the artistic, avant-garde beatnik set discovered it and began feeding it to the white middle class. The poems of Ginsberg and Jack Kerouac lauded its effects. Today's hippies took the ugly, flowering plant from the dropouts and beatniks and, with a flair that still leaves Madison Avenue stung, built this universal staple of their life into a sweet pleasure which they say all people should be able to experience at will. Thousands upon thousands of young people have been sold.

Over the years, the anti-pot arguments of the Federal Bureau of Narcotics have shifted with the plant's image. Statements that marijuana leads to sex and violence are currently passé. Now the claim—a false one—is that marijuana leads to heroin use, but the kids will have none of this.

Marijuana is easy to obtain, as Eve Babitz, an East Village hippie, told Sen. Quentin Burdick of South Dakota at a Senate subcommittee hearing in the summer of 1967.

"This may be a futile question," Burdick said, "but where do you get your marijuana cigarettes?"

"Everybody," Eve replied.

"Pardon?"

"Everybody. Everybody I know. I mean, just about everybody I know except for my grandmother and my grandfather smokes marijuana."

Teeny boppers in Corona, Queens, New York also found marijuana easy to obtain. When they wanted kicks, they sought licks. This came to light when police charged that the manager of a Carvel ice cream stand wrapped pot in cellophane bags, placed it into his cones below the scoops of ice cream, and sold the cones for five dollars apiece.

After alcohol, marijuana is the most popular intoxicant in the world. The United Nations reported that a 1950 survey indicated that 200 million persons in the world puffed pot. And as the popularity of pot has grown, the controversy about it has become in the medical world what the Vietnam war is to politics. From UCLA to Harvard, smoking pot has become a normal part of the college experience. Small, intimate pot parties are even becoming more fashionable among lawyers, writers, artists, doctors and corporation executives who want to escape, temporarily, from the prison of their 9 to 5 lives.

What are the reasons for this wave of popularity? Why turn on with marijuana? The answers are manifold and vital. They are the answers to tomorrow's generation, born into a fast world from which there is no escape.

"Our Thing"

POT IS part of a youthful cultural revolution. Its popularity could prove no different than the alcohol revolution among the young of the 1920's or the campus sexual revolution of the 1940's and 1950's. It could be the answer of the 1960's to that need in youth to test the new and forbidden. But it may be more than that. Some observers see in pot the signs of a permanent shift in American social habits, from the bottom up. The age of frontiers is ended, at least on this planet. There is little left for youth to explore but their inner workings.

Whether pot is a fad or a social shift will have to await the judgment of history. There is a basic restlessness among space-age youth. It was given flame and a hero in John F. Kennedy. It turned toward the Peace Corps, attacked poverty and promoted the arts. Then came the assassination and, later, the escalation of Vietnam. An undefinable spirit was lost, or at least subdued, but the future seems to promise a reawakening.

The Popularity of Pot

Pot is part of today's scene. It is too easy to play the numbers game and estimate how many use marijuana. The zoom of pot to popularity is a phenomenon that few of the older generation (those over 30) can understand. Parents believe that marijuana's affluence is an ominous threat to society as they know it. Youth responds that it is a means to break the frustrating restrictions of that society.

Youth is leaping society's barriers in growing numbers. The *New York Post,* in a definitive series on marijuana in October, 1967, said there are between 250,000 and 1,000,000 regular or occasional users in New York City alone, and it estimated that up to 30% of college students at major universities in New York and San Francisco have tried pot at least once—figures that have been confirmed by other surveys. According to the aforementioned Associated Press survey of several New England colleges, at least a third of the undergraduates tried pot at least once (although only a few turned out to be regular potheads).

The *Post* series interviewed a pot peddler who claimed he had made quantity sales at Harvard, Yale, NYU, Fairleigh Dickinson, Barnard, Cornell, Buffalo and Bennington. This same dealer also said that his off-campus customers included not only hippies but lawyers, doctors, psychiatrists, morticians, rabbis, priests, carpenters, truck drivers, actors, musicians, assistant district attorneys and police officers!

Students at New York colleges (St. John's, New York University, Pratt, Columbia, Brooklyn College and the City University of New York) have "gone to pot" in a big way, as the *New York Daily News* found in a recent survey. It sent teams of youthful reporters who could pass for students to each campus to talk and listen. Student users again estimated that 30% of their number turn on with marijuana. NYU was rated the most hip, and St. John's, along with Brooklyn

College, the most square. Some 40% of those asked at NYU smoked pot, while only 6.3% did so at Brooklyn College.

The story is the same at Harvard where university psychiatrists estimated that at least 25% of the freshman class had tried pot. A recent Princeton University survey of 3,200 undergraduates came up with a 15% figure for those who had lit up at least once. The use at Yale is either 20% or 35%, depending on whether the school's survey or the student's survey is read.

While college use of marijuana appears to be widespread, its use is not limited to higher education. One revealing survey took place at the two high schools of the upper-middle-class Long Island community of Great Neck. Some 8% of the 2,600 students questioned admitted using marijuana, and significantly, 25% favored the legalization of pot.

If arrest figures are any indicator, fashionable Westchester County in New York, which has more millionaires per square mile than any other U.S. county except for New York County (Manhattan), has witnessed a significant increase in the use of pot. The county has followed the trend to upper-middle-class pot puffing with arrests up from 309 in 1965 to 700 in 1966.

A truckload of other figures could be dumped on these pages, but their trend would be little different from the numbers already cited. What is clear is the extremely widespread use of marijuana.

Why Does Youth Take Drugs?

All of the youths who lie behind these statistics are not taking drugs just for kicks. Many are doing it out of a sense of disillusionment with ugliness and hypocrisy in the real world, according to Professor Leonard Wolf of San Francisco State. And as one Cornell senior put it, most university students have the feeling that there is no God, and that all the works of man will have no meaning when life is done.

In an address to the American Psychiatric Association on May 11, 1966, Dr. Seymour Halleck, director of student psychiatry at the University of Wisconsin, described the use of marijuana and LSD as part of a pattern of alienation and hostility in the students whom he treats. He characterized the alienated student as one with an ill-defined self-concept: "Late adolescence is a period in which young people struggle to find a solid identity. Sometimes conflicts . . . are serious enough so that the student experiences an identity crisis, a sense of profound uncertainty as to who he is, where he comes from and where he is going. The alienated student can be described as existing in a state of chronic identity crises." These unhappy students—Halleck places their number at about 4%—seek to create a "new inner reality simply by taking a pill or smoking a marijuana cigarette." Marijuana, he asserted, has become "a rallying cause for students, a challenge to adults and a potent catalyst for widening the gap between generations."

This is one of several explanations that students give for using marijuana. About half a dozen reasons occur over and over again. Those who respond with their reasons are mostly in the mainstream of student life. Generally, they are bright, hard-working students who maintain A and B averages.

The pot scene is very much like an iceberg. Society sees only the very visible portion, the long-haired, "weirdo" hippies and the dropouts who linger around campus centers. However, most of those who use marijuana regularly or occasionally are typical campus types. They are clean-cut, well dressed, and above average in classroom ability and in the size of their parents' bank accounts. They are the fraternity brothers and sorority sisters, athletes, future lawyers and scientists, musicians and artists.

Most numerous among the campus users are those who go up, up and away once a week at most. Their attitude to the pot experience partly helps explain its popularity. A St. John's University (New York) junior felt that his weekend "flights" were a social gesture, "like offering a friend a drink," while a Harvard graduate saw it as just another in life's experiences, "like a first drink or the first sexual experience." The latter found marijuana relaxing, a pleasant diversion that was also aesthetically rewarding. Far from being objectionable, he regarded it as just another engaging distraction, like skiing.

While there is considerable medical evidence to prove that the Harvard graduate's conclusions are erroneous, his attitude is shared by a vast body of today's youth. The tuned-in generation claims that adults are hypocrites, damning marijuana while turning on with booze, tranquilizers, barbiturates and diet pills. Youth has issued a challenge to the society that profits from nicotine, caffeine and alcohol while saying that marijuana is wrong. They assert that marijuana is less likely to cause trouble than alcohol and is therefore far less dangerous. "If my parents drink three martinis before dinner," one youth said, "then why can't I take pot?" To the children of the atomic age, born into a disordered world, marijuana is their thing, uncorrupted by the "alcohol generation."

In a sense, the marijuana revolution is the latest progression of America's drugged society. Adults use asprin for headaches, penicillin for infections and amphetamines and barbiturates if they want to feel happy or depressed. For the teeny bopper set the purchase of pot and its use is often only for kicks. It's a party thing, something done in parental defiance or simply in search of a new forbidden thrill. Often it's done only because the gang's doing it. One Brooklyn bopper playground was located in the apartment of a 15-year-old girl whose parents were away. Guests at her marijuana party consisted of 16 girls and 11 boys between the ages of 12 and 18. They came from Erasmus Hall and Prospect Heights High Schools and Walt Whitman Junior High School.

Similar parties crop up in headlines nearly every week. A real winging recently took place in Fairfield, Connecticut, where 69 teenage sons and daughters of the suburban affluent were nabbed at a party where marijuana was found. Still another ended abruptly with the help of police in Roslyn Heights, Long Island, where two 16-year-old girls and three boys of the same age, all students in an expensive Connecticut private school, were found puffing pot. But what is especially frightening is the fact that for every pot party crashed by the law, dozens are thrown without interference.

Pot has become a symbol in the war of the under-30 group with their elders. It is symbolic of discontent with many basic American values, and specifically with the cherished ideals of middle-class society. A British newsman in New York asked: "Why don't they just legalize the bloody stuff and end the fuss?" It is true that legalization might end the fuss, much as acceptance of beatnik coffee shops killed their attraction. However, it might also open the floodgates to another social addiction, as happened when the use of tobacco and alcohol became fashionable.

Aside from the considerable number of pure thrillseekers and the "defy mommy and daddy" set, many young people regard pot as a means to stop the world and get off for a moment. Dropping out of school to think things over is out; you'll get drafted. However, according to youth, the pot experience is restful, for it increases friendliness and creates, if only for the moment, some peace in a frustrating world.

The doors of challenge to America's youth are mostly slammed shut. A challenge is still there in the classroom and on the job, but a large number of young people are bored with this routine. This group takes for granted that there will be food and jobs. They want "meaningful" experiences, and frequently they claim that they find it in pot.

This mental attitude may explain what McGlothlin means when he wrote in *Psychedelic Review:* "Users almost invariably report the motivation to attain a 'high' feeling which is generally described as a 'feeling of adequacy and efficiency' in which mental conflicts are allayed.... The experienced user is able to achieve consistently a state of self-confidence, satisfaction and relaxation."

Tom is a 21-year-old Harvard junior with a B average. He in no way conforms to the hippie image; rather, he looks like the corporate lawyer he hopes to be. Booze left him cold; it did nothing for the knots in his stomach before exams. Then, at the end of his freshman year, depressed by the thought of final exams, he tried pot. It relaxed him, warmed him and made things a bit easier to take.

Dan, a 19-year-old sophomore at Princeton, started to take pot for similar reasons, but with a broader explanation. In his view of society, he is a circus ringmaster, and its demands are the hurdles that he must clear to get his peanuts. Dan found that marijuana afforded him a means of release, a chance to sit back and understand.

Where will the marijuana revolution lead? Literary critic Leslie Fiedler, who was arrested in 1967 on pot charges, feels that the old world is breaking up and a new one is in birth: "Young people are in the process of redefining the line which divides the psychotic from the sane."

The Pot Party

The word had spread quickly among the members of the in-set at the NYU cafeteria—there was going to be a pot party Saturday night at Lisa's pad in the fashionable East 80's of Manhattan. As we walked along the hallway to the door of her 9th-floor apartment, the sounds of drums and other percussion instruments grew insistently louder.

We groped through a bluish haze lit by a solitary red lamp. Lisa bounded from the rug to usher us in as George bellowed a mournful wail about Vietnam war orphans. The 80-degree heat in the low-ceilinged room pressed in on us as the rock music and psychedelic posters plastering the wall assaulted our ears and eyes.

"You're just in time," Lisa gurgled.

Everyone was there—Steve, who worked as a children's counselor in a city park, Sue and Sugar, twin coeds, several married couples, John, who was a long-haired government worker, and a dozen more.

The hilarity subsided as the communal pipe, with a large bowl and curled stem, was tamped full of marijuana and wrapped in tinfoil. As the pipe made the ceremonial rounds, everyone inhaled as much smoke as he could deep into his lungs and held it there for as long as possible without breathing. Immediately afterward, a few pot cigarettes were passed around until they could no longer be held with the fingers. Then tweezers appeared and the roaches were relished until they could no longer be used. As the last bitty end was about to fall, Sugar took it into her bare hands, popped it into her mouth and swallowed it while it was still burning.

Lisa and John shared a joint. They rolled up an empty matchbook cover and inserted the cigarette into it to get a "supercharge," one that would mingle more carbon dioxide with the marijuana smoke and get pot's active chemical into the bloodstream more quickly. John put the lit end of the rigged cigarette into his mouth, inhaled and held the smoke. He blew it back through the cigarette and the matchbook tube as Lisa took a drag from the other end.

Restraint eventually melted into frank conversation. Sue expressed her hatred for the Vietnam war. Steve likened his pot experience to a fast elevator ride and said that he likes to eat marijuana before dinner because it whets his appetite. Sugar said she just loved everybody when she was on grass. Someone turned down the stereo as the talk turned to psychedelic art produced under pot's influence.

Gradually, with the assistance of additional rounds of pot, speech thickened and attention spans were shortened as each pothead sank into a world of senses. Ideas became hazy and the scene was tranquil. Gradually the party's guests drifted from the pad.

Each guest at the party had a different level of experience, for pot's effects vary with the individual personality and the setting in which it is used as well as with its strength. Some find it a disappointment, a mild pleasure exaggerated by friends. One girl was frightened by her first marijuana cigarette which she smoked in a dingy room among strangers. But her next trip, made in her own home, was pleasurable.

What Is It Like?

What is the marijuana experience like? The answer to this question explains in part why so many seek its promise of new adventure in the as yet uncharted inner world of the mind.

Once inhaled, marijuana smoke is held as long as possible to gain the effect. An experienced pot cigarette smoker can control its effects at will by regulating his intake, and with repeated doses he can produce exactly the degree of exhilaration he seeks. He will have no difficulty with such control in maintaining his feeling of well-being, contentment, sociability and mental and physical relaxation.

Physically, there is a sharp speedup in the heartbeat, dilation of the pupils, reddening of the eyelids and muscular looseness. Drowsiness grows. The pothead appears to be mildly intoxicated and often laughs and giggles without apparent cause. His sense of time is distorted and parts of the body seem to shorten or grow. The ability to judge and remember shrinks. For some, there may be hallucinations, and others may become so hungry that they could empty a refrigerator in a few minutes. Still others feel a greater sexual urge, but this is due more to a release of inhibitions than to any boost in the sex drive.

Poet Ginsberg, long an advocate of marijuana use and a founder of an organization to legalize marijuana, wrote that pot "shifts the center of attention from habitual, shallow, purely verbal guidelines and repetitive second-hand ideological interpretations of experience to more direct, slower, absorbing, occasionally microscopically minute engagements with sensing phenomena during the high." And in *On the Road,* Jack Kerouac wrote: "The bouncing was no longer unpleasant; it was the most pleasant and graceful billowy trip in the world, as over a blue sea. . . . The bouncing sent shivers of ecstasy through me. I saw streams of gold pouring through the sky, and Mexico was a glittering treasure box."

Marijuana's active chemical, cannabinol, alters consciousness in a more radical way than alcohol's dulling effect. Dr. Dana Farnsworth, director of Harvard's University's Health Services, noted that, in a manner much like LSD, ideas are rapid, disconnected and uncontrollable, and that grass may cause moodiness, fear of death and panic.

While superficially innocent, marijuana's real danger lies in its hidden effects. Continued use causes a loss of interest in many other aspects of life for many potheads. It can produce a reduction of drive toward goals or provide an easy escape for those who won't confront life's problems. This psychological dependence on marijuana for a release from today's mad world is one that concerns doctors considerably.

"What worries me," said Yale psychologist Keniston, "is the state of the nation where the most exciting thing available to the brightest young people is marijuana. After all, pot is a pretty poor kick, a poor substitute for real, active, exciting, meaningful experience. My complaint with marijuana is not that it hurts the smoker physically, but that it turns this bright young person away from society and robs society of his talents and energies."

Danger Signals

T HE POT and anti-pot forces are currently locked in
   a bitter struggle that a few moderates who have
kept their cool are trying to resolve. As the controversy
grows in intensity, each combatant is dead certain that
he is right, but the solution will probably emerge from
the moderate camp.

Some Important Questions

The major source of the conflict is the set of contra-
dictory answers given by each camp to the following
questions: Do users develop a psychological dependence
on marijuana that is even more difficult to overcome
than physical dependence? Does pot cause psychotic
episodes or long-range personality changes? Does
chronic use damage the brain and other organs? Is
marijuana a stepping-stone to heroin? Does pot cause
violent crime and sexual excess? In short, just how
dangerous is marijuana?

The problem is twofold. First of all, most of the
scientific evidence available comes from nations like
India where highly potent forms of the hemp plant are
used. These studies are not considered applicable to
the American problem because of our preference for
marijuana, which is the weakling of the cannibis family.
Second, no one has yet discovered exactly what part of

97

the brain pot affects and precisely what it does, mainly because of the difficulty of synthesizing or simulating hemp's active ingredient, cannibol, in sufficient quantities to conduct proper studies.

However, the rapidly increasing popularity of marijuana throughout the nation may eventually provide the answers. The federal government, which is always reluctant to move its ponderous machinery without a public outcry, has finally heard the word. In fiscal 1966-1967 the National Institute of Mental Health granted more than $450,000 for private research programs to determine the chemical nature of pot and its physical and psychological effects, and Dr. Cole, chief of the psycho-pharmocology research branch of the Institute, expects that sum to be tripled in the next few years. In addition, Dr. Tod Mikuriya, formerly of the New Jersey Psychiatric Institute, is coordinating 11 projects directly related to marijuana. Moreover, the Institute has eight studies of its own underway, including one to investigate the possible beneficial medical uses of the drug.

Further projects currently underway include one by Dr. Raphael Mechoulam of the Hadassah Medical School of the Hebrew University in Jerusalem, Israel, to isolate and synthesize marijuana's active ingredients. Others worthy of mention are probes into the effects of marijuana compounds on the central nervous system, a study of the effects of pot's components on animals and a survey to accurately determine the drug's popularity and to gather information of the social, mental and physical results of its use.

Until now, such laboratory research was difficult

because marijuana was a plant form. Mechoulam made the major breakthrough by synthesizing some of pot's ingredients in amounts useful for research. Working with an American team headed by Dr. Herchel Smith of Wyeth Laboratories, Inc., Philadelphia, Mechoulam and his assistants developed a practical method for artificially reproducing two intoxicating ingredients of marijuana. In separate reports in the *Journal of the American Chemical Society* during the summer of 1967, these scientists asserted that this development opened the way to a much greater understanding of how the smoke from marijuana acts on the body as a whole, how it affects the brain and whether it has additional side effects.

An intriguing question yet to be answered concerns marijuana's potential as a beneficial drug. It is already recognized as an appetite stimulant, and because of its ability to release inhibitions, it has helped in the treatment of depressed mental patients. There is some speculation that it could be used to quell migraine headaches, and it may also hold promise as a pain-killer that is less harmful than morphine, an addictive opium drug. Moreover, Princeton University studies indicate that it may possibly be employed to lower body temperatures, increase low pulse rates, kill bacteria, stimulate the kidneys and eventually yield a whole new class of drugs.

One use for marijuana, to stimulate creative drive, and profound thought, is very much overrated. While regular users may feel that they have gained greater insights through its use, the drug actually depresses these abilities. As Dr. Robert S. Liebert, Columbia University psychiatric consultant, has noted: "When I talk to a kid who is turned on, I have the sense of relating through a glass partition."

Marijuana and Heroin

A typical example of the mythology that studies by the National Institute of Mental Health seek to dispel took place in Buffalo, New York, on March 16, 1967. Patrick P. Carroll, assistant commissioner of the Federal Bureau of Narcotics, told his audience of a study which indicated that 96% of Harlem youngsters who use heroin were introduced to narcotics by smoking marijuana. He thus implied that marijuana smokers grow up to become heroin shooters. However, according to the President's Crime Commission, although there is evidence that a majority of heroin users have experienced marijuana, "this does not mean that one leads to the other in the sense that marijuana has an intrinsic quality that creates a heroin liability. There is no scientific basis for such a theory. . . . There are too many marijuana users who do not graduate to heroin, and too many heroin users with no known prior marijuana use, to support such a theory."

This position has been borne out repeatedly. Bruce Jackson, now with the State University of New York at Buffalo, made a three-year study of middle-class adult marijuana users in New York, Boston and Austin, Texas—cities in which pot puffing is widespread. He reported that there was no evidence that marijuana led to use of more powerful drugs. In addition, he found no necessary link to sexual promiscuity, violence or crime.

Heroin users themselves reject the idea of such a link. As one of them commented, the use of marijuana does not satisfy the H-shooter, for pot arouses the senses while heroin calms and deadens them. Another heroin addict said that even if he had never smoked marijuana, he would still have turned to heroin: "I had a severe character disorder that had to come out. Marijuana wasn't a stepping-stone for me."

As opposed to heroin, marijuana is not addictive. Pot does not cause a physical craving that turns its users into animals on the prowl for the next dose, for that needle slipped under the skin which will ward off the severe withdrawal pains for another four hours. Moreover, the pothead's body does not demand ever increasing amounts of marijuana to achieve the same satisfaction. The strong psychological dependence felt by heroin users is usually absent. A marijuana user can quit at will, although he does have a desire to reexperience marijuana's effects.

The idea that marijuana sends its users on violent rampages is without foundation. It is true that reports by the Federal Bureau of Narcotics asserted that there was a clear link between marijuana and violence, and that link may actually exist. But it must be remembered that the Bureau deliberately seeks out evidence of such links. Its field manual orders district supervisors to keep in close touch with local officials "for the purpose of obtaining detailed reports in all cases involving violation of local marijuana laws where crimes were committed while under the influence of marijuana." On the other hand, however, according to the President's Crime Commission report, published in 1967, statements indicating that criminals were under the influence of marijuana while committing crimes may be "self-serving." The Commission felt that marijuana "might, but certainly will not necessarily or inevitably lead to aggressive behavior or crime," and it asserted that "the response will depend more on the individual than on the drug."

Despite persistent reports that "you can groove better with someone when you're stoned," to use the expression of a Queens College, New York, junior, marijuana does not intensify sexual pleasure. As a matter of fact, most college students who were questioned reported a diminished sex urge when using pot, and this is borne out in studies made by Dr. Richard Blum of Stanford's Institute for the Study of Human Problems and many other experts. In a 1965 issue of *Psychedelic Review,* McGlothlin asserted that marijuana's mythical ability to heighten sex drive is not due to any aphrodisiac quality it may possess but "to the reduction of inhibition and increased suggestibility" that it produces, and he further stated that marijuana is probably "little, if any, more effective than alcohol in this respect."

The Disastrous Effects of Marijuana

With the marijuana myths displayed for what they are, we can now take a reasoned, unhysterical look at some of the real harm that cannabis can cause. However, it must first be remembered that marijuana research is still in its infancy. There must be a great deal of further investigation and study before the effects of marijuana and the relative safety or danger of its use can be accurately determined.

According to a World Health Organization bulletin, although there is "no unequivocal evidence" that pot reduces lasting mental changes, harm resulting from its use may include "lethargy, inertia, self-neglect, the feeling of increased capability with corresponding failure, and, in some cases, the precipitation of psychotic episodes." On the other hand, physical deterioration among American users of hemp is virtually nonexistent. Dr. David Lewis of Beth Israel Hospital, Boston, who is a specialist in internal medicine, has testified that studies of 200 potheads showed no physical damage. The only symptom he noted was a slower heartbeat and a reddening of the eyes while under the influence of marijuana. Other doctors have reported the occurrence of respiratory illnesses such as bronchitis among heavy users, but this is a symptom that is also characteristic of those who smoke more normal forms of tobacco.

Nevertheless, these observations merely scratch the surface. The key question is the effect of a specific amount of marijuana on a user, and up to this time the most significant results in marijuana research have resulted from probing the possibilities of psychotic reactions. An American-Israeli team of scientists recently scored a major breakthrough by devising an economical synthesis of tetrahydracannabinol (THC), believed to be the chief intoxicant in marijuana. Research following the breakthrough demonstrated that psychotic reactions can occur. Moreover, studies at the Federal Addiction Research Center, Lexington, Kentucky, proved that a sufficient amount of THC can cause a psychotic reaction in every user. Dr. Harris Isbell of the University of Kentucky, who is collaborating on the research, told the *New York Times* on October 9, 1967: "I can make anybody fly with enough THC."

About 25 micrograms of THC were given to each subject in the Lexington tests for each two pounds of body weight. This amount caused a happy, even silly and relaxed feeling. Time sense and preception were distorted when the dosage was upped to 100 micrograms. At 200 micrograms, most subjects underwent psychotic reactions akin to those effected by LSD: illusions, delusions and hallucinations. One man saw himself shrivel down to doll size and then watched his own funeral. At 480 micrograms, all subjects experienced psychotic episodes. It was also demonstrated that psychotic reactions can occur with relatively low doses of THC.

The Lexington investigators concluded that "psychotic reactions after smoking marijuana under the usual conditions in the United States appear to be rare, but the low incidence of such psychotic breaks may reflect nothing more than the low THC content of most of the marijuana available in the United States."

The number of potheads who currently use marijuana in sufficient strength and frequently enough to be in constant danger of freaking out is below 5%. Their reactions differ only in degree from those who use the far more dangerous LSD. But The American Medical Association, in an August 1967 statement, warned that repeated use of large amounts of marijuana may result in "illusions and delusions that predispose to antisocial behavior, sleep disturbance, impaired coordination, chronic bronchitis and asthma, low blood sugar, confusion and irritability." And McGlothlin has asserted that "virtually all of the phenomena associated with LSD also are, or can be, produced by cannibis. This includes bodily distortion, depersonalization, hallucinations and, in some cases, paranoid reactions."

Many doctors believe that legalization of marijuana

would not swell the ranks of chronic users. Dr. David Powelson, chief of psychiatric services at the University of California at Berkeley, noted that marijuana is now generally available and still only a relative few use it.

Social Questions

What of the social problems connected with the use of marijuana? A study of dangerous drugs and social policy by Blum, contained in the 1967 Presidential Crime Commission's Task Force on Law Enforcement and Administration report, stated: "Mind-altering drug use in the United States is nearly universal, most of it by individuals without causing danger to others." Blum's definition of such drugs included a variety of preparations ranging from aspirin, coffee and tea through tranquilizers, sedatives, stimulants, strong painkillers like morphine, "popular social drugs such as alcohol and tobacco, illicit but relatively harmless—as presently used—social drugs as marijuana and peyote," and the problem drugs including heroin and LSD.

The book *Drug Abuse, Escape to Nowhere,* issued in 1967 by Smith, Kline and French Laboratories in conjunction with the National Education Association, said that "in terms of some effects on behavior, use of marijuana is roughly comparable to moderate use of alcohol. . . . Like alcohol, it tends to loosen inhibitions and increase suggestibility, which explains why an individual under the influence of marijuana may engage in activities he would not ordinarily consider." After noting that marijuana does not produce physical dependence or tolerance, the book warned that "moderate to strong psychic dependence can develop."

"Naive and ill-informed" is the label that Dr.

Benjamin Kissin attaches to hippies, college students and teeny boppers who believe marijuana to be a harmless stimulant with no habit-forming effects. Kissin, director of the Alcoholism Division of the Psychiatry Department of Downstate Medical Center, Brooklyn, wrote in the June 1967 issue of the *Downstate Reporter* that pot, far from being a safe lark, can cause a state of psychic dependence that may be stronger than physical addiction, and that psychic dependence can result "in the most intensive craving and perpetuation of compulsive abuse."

In August 1967, the American Medical Association took this a step further, asserting that such dependence is an almost universal symptom of "serious underlying personality problems, severe neurotic conflicts or psychotic reactions." It called marijuana a medical problem "because its use is probably disproportionately higher among young persons with developing psychiatric problems than among those without them," and it stated that during treatment the main task "is to learn from the patient what really bothers him at both conscious and unconscious levels, and what needs are being spuriously met at both these levels by taking marijuana."

As far back as 1944 a committee formed by New York City Mayor Fiorello LaGuardia ridiculed the idea that all marijuana users were raving sex maniacs and murderers. The internists, psychiatrists, pharmacologists, public health experts and policemen who formed the group likened pot's dangers to those posed by alcohol. The LaGuardia committee was roundly damned for its conclusions, but it planted the seed that led to today's studies and resultant new attitudes on the drug. Its report also helped to spawn highly vocal

roups who now agitate for marijuana's legalization,
laiming—falsely—that it is completely harmless.

hould Marijuana Be Legalized?

Before today's hippies stole the show, LEMAR
whose initials stand for "Legalize Marijuana) had
nade most of the headlines in the legalization drive.
ed by beatnik poets Allen Ginsberg and Peter Orlov-
ky, LEMAR puts out leaflets and stages demonstra-
ons, using the following theory as its underlying basis:
If we can have alcohol and cigarettes, why not mari-
uana?" And apparently a majority of students across
he United States share LEMAR's view. The student
ewspapers of Michigan, Yale, Boston, Wisconsin,
uffalo and Colorado Universities—to name but a few
—have recommended that pot be legalized, as has the
National Student Association.

At the gut of the legalization question is the harsh
aw itself. Some seek outright repeal; others would
often its harsh penalties, basing their stand on the basis
hat marijuana is a relatively mild drug; still others want
o keep the present law intact. The Marijuana Tax Act
tipulates that anyone possessing pot must register with
he Secretary of the Treasury, fill out official forms and
ay a levy of $1 per ounce of hemp. Only 88 persons,
pparently engaged in medicine or research, are licensed
o use marijuana. As previously noted, possession with-
ut registration brings severe penalties.

One effect of the law may be an increase in the use
of marijuana, inasmuch as pot smoking has been driven
nderground. Thus it has acquired the aura of for-
idden fruit and attracted many, especially the teeny
et, as a fertile means of rebellion against parents and

society. Early in 1966, in an address to the Institute for the Study of Drug Addiction, Louria urged that "unrealistic laws" against the use of marijuana be toned down, as he asserted: "Marijuana is essentially a minor league offense. It should be treated as a hallucinogen, rather than as a narcotic, as it is today." In the same vein, Goddard has expressed his personal feelings on the subject as a physician, stating: "The severity of the penalties is inconsistent with the nature of the drug itself."

These two statements might appear to be an endorsement for the abolition of penalties for the use of marijuana, but Louria has also expressed what is probably the closest thing to a consensus among scientists and medical men today: "We must not overreact to marijuana use, but we cannot afford to legalize it." He then added: "Our society has opted for enough escape mechanisms already—liquor, caffeine and cigarettes. Why not let everyone have two barbiturates a day or two amphetamines? You have to draw the line." And Dr. Lawrence Kolb, former assistant surgeon general of the U.S. Public Health Service, and a leading authority on alcoholism, basically echoed Louria when he stated: "Alcohol during the past 2,500 years has apparently become an irreplacable part of our social structure. We know that it does much harm, but the fact that we tolerate this harm is no reason for permitting the indiscriminate use of another intoxicant. . . . Legalization would have profound social effects. Even now, while pot is illegal, its social effects are apparent. One frequent indicator of the heavy use of pot observed by physicians is neglect of personal hygiene and nutrition. Marijuana also induces lethargy and sloth that drops many productive youngsters from society."

The scientific evidence of the immediate and long-range effects of marijuana will ultimately determine whether or not the drug will be legalized. The first reports are already trickling in, and what they have to say does not offer much reason for encouragement to the LEMAR set and their successors. However, even though the final conclusions have not been reached there is sufficient evidence now that warns of danger. The would-be pot puffer should be aware of this evidence. To ignore it is foolish. Marijuana is not a fun thing.

Mind-Twisting
Tidbits

IN THE small Michigan community of Westland, the tombstones of 8-year-old Deborah Louise Crowther and her younger sister, Kimberly Faith, offer mute testimony to the effects of glue-sniffing. On April 29, 1967, their bloodstained, nude bodies were found in a field close to their home. They had been sexually attacked and strangled with their own tiny stockings as they returned from school.

Near their bodies were found 15 tubes of the type of glue favored by sniffers. On August 15, their killer, a 14-year-old boy identified by two young brothers who witnessed part of the brutal attack, was found innocent of murder on the grounds that glue-sniffing had rendered him temporarily insane. Detroit Juvenile Court Judge James H. Lincoln said that the boy, who had run away from home, was "incapable of controlling his actions at the time of the killings." Supporting his decision was the statement of psychiatrists at the time of the crime that if a person harbors latent violence, glue-sniffing could cause a shedding of inhibitions and permit acts that would not otherwise be committed.

Dangerous Fads

Glue, LSD and marijuana, the most famous hallucogens, are the most widely used among youth today. But there are scores of other mind-twisting tidbits that appeal to limited groups. They include such way-out substances as anti-freeze, hair tonic, gasoline and even a chemical used to frost cocktail glasses. Among the elders of the chemical set, such drugs as peyote, sacred mushroom, mescaline, DMT and STP are in use. Favorites among the youngest of teeny boppers are lighter fluid and airplane glue.

Far too many parents tend to lightly dismiss the fact that their barely teenage youngsters sniff glue. When they were young, they slipped aspirin into cokes for kicks. However, glue can kick the stuffings out of a youth who is "just being a boy." The first sniffs of glue cause dizziness, and further whiffs bring on a stupor. Severe hallucinations follow, and vomiting and unconsciousness often result from continued heavy inhaling. In some cases, the bone marrow, liver, kidneys, brain or heart can suffer severe damage, and in a surprisingly short time. Moreover, an added danger of glue-sniffing, as with so many other drugs, is that an enjoyed experience can lead the user to other, even more dangerous drugs, just to see what kicks they hold.

Sniffers frequently are attracted by fads. A recent one involved a coolant of the type used to frost cocktail glasses. It was a passing thing in the chemical kaleidoscope that reportedly cropped up at Reed College in Portland, Oregon, and was tried out at Yale University. The whole thing probably would have gone unnoticed if it were not for the death of 11-year-old Lucy R.

White in Greenwich, Connecticut in October 1967. The girl's mother said that Lucy's 17-year-old brother John had filled a balloon with the freezing substance, and that Lucy had put it to her mouth and inhaled. As a result her larynx froze and she was unable to breathe. Investigating police found that youths had been buying the chemical at a local hardware store and inhaling it for its effects of cutting the oxygen intake and causing a tingling sensation.

In almost every kitchen, readily available is still another hallucogen—nutmeg, the East Indian spice used to flavor foods. After special preparation, its use causes a feeling of lightheartedness or floating. It can also make the user drowsy. Heavy users of the special preparation of nutmeg can experience a rapid heartbeat, excessive thirst, strong agitation and even panic reactions.

Anti-freeze, gasoline, hair tonic, lighter fluid and other such substances have much the same effects as glue-sniffing. The key to the prevention of their misuse —you can't make the purchase of gasoline a crime—is the knowledge that these chemicals are dangerous, even deadly. Teenagers owe it to themselves to learn just what these hallucogens can do.

Morning Glory Seeds and Banana Peels

Morning glory seeds, whose effects last longer and are more vivid than those produced by marijuana, have never become very popular as a hallucogen in this country because of their foul taste, the nausea they effect and the lengthy and potentially dangerous extraction procedure necessary to release their active chemical, lysergic acid amide. The seeds, from the morning glory vines that flower so profusely across the United States, can be purchased in any garden shop or from any seed company. However, as a safeguard, the contents of the little paper packets with the colorful flowers on the front have been treated to cause even greater nausea when eaten. The seeds can be made into a mush which has a bitter taste and causes strong nausea, or their active agent can be extracted with the aid of such a highly dangerous chemical as wood alcohol.

One amusing interlude in the dizzy, demented world of hallucogens was the brief banana peel craze. A Berkeley, California hippie sheet reported, tongue-in-cheek, that scraped and toasted banana peels, when pounded into a powder and smoked, produced a "mild high" similar to the effects of marijuana. Banana cigarettes immediately became the rage. "Some people sell wooden nickles; I sell banana smokes," said Larry Starin, whose "Mellow Yellow" firm made a fortune on the hoax. The whole thing was ridiculous. It was simply a fun thing to do, and a hit record even developed as a result of the craze.

Peyote and Mescaline

However, most of the odd-ball hallucogens do not have such amusing results—for example, the bitter tasting, dried buttons of the peyote cactus which are chewed or chopped and brewed into tea. Their use is legal, thanks to a U.S. Supreme Court ruling, provided that you are an American Indian and a member of the Native American Church.

Mexican Indians have used peyote for several years to obtain visions for supernatural revelations. Their

Spanish masters enforced Christianity on the basis that they wished to eradicate paganism, but the shrewd Mexican Indians managed to blend both into what has become the Native American Church, and the use of peyote as a religious sacramental spread to the Indians of the American West in the 1870's.

The active hallucogen in the small peyote cactus grown in northern Mexico and in parts of the Rio Grands Valley of the Southwest is mescaline. Since the Indians only use peyote intermittently in religious ceremonies, there is little evidence of long-term effects. However, regular use of the drug will cause acute psychotic reactions.

The use of peyote among the psychedelic set has never been widespread, mainly because of its bitter taste and the nausea it causes. In addition, mescaline, which ignites peyote's visions, is stronger when taken alone, and it does not have the more distasteful side effects. The hallucinations from mescaline may last as long as 16 hours. Normally, the mescaline experience is one of geometric visions. But it is possible for the drug to cause a psychosis much in the same way as LSD. One man who was high on mescaline believed that he was a fly crawling upside down on the ceiling. He moved with great caution, feeling that if he moved too quickly he would crash to the floor below.

The crackdown on the sale and possession of LSD may signal wider use of mescaline, which is now rather limited because it can cause some nausea. Moreover, the availability of peyote heightens its potential for use.

The Sacred Mushroom

Psilocybin, psilocybe mexicana, or the Mexican

sacred mushroom, is the drug that launched Dr. Timothy Leary and the psychedelic movement. Along with LSD, it was used in the historic Harvard experiments that led to the sacking of Leary and Alpert.

Centuries before Leary, magic mushrooms were used by the Indians of southern Mexico in religious rites that survive to this day, although they are now a strange mixture of Christian and pagan ceremony. The simple altars adorned with images of Christ and the saints found in the thatched adobe homes where the rites are performed during the night are a concession to the Spanish rule that lingers to this day.

Psilocybin, the active drug in the sacred mushroom, was first synthesized in the 1950's. However, use of magic mushroom was a tightly kept sacret until recently when R. Gordon Wasson—who with his late wife, Valentina, spent 30 years studying mushrooms—and Allan Richardson, took part in a ceremony at the tiny village of Huautla in Oaxaca Province. In a magazine article in *Life,* Wasson reported his experience.

About 20 men, women and children had gathered in the evening darkness, dressed in their Sunday best. (The children were simply present for the occasion but were not to be given any of the drug.) A middle-aged woman, the priestess who was to lead the rite, first brushed away the dirt from the sacred mushrooms. Then, with prayers, she passed them through the smoke of resin incense which rose from the floor. Finally, seated on a mat on the floor before the simple altar, she passed out the mushrooms, always in pairs.

Wasson and Richardson chewed their mushrooms for 30 minutes. They tasted acrid and had a persistent rancid odor. After a short time, colors became razor-sharp and visions began. The lights were put out and the priestess began singing softly. From time to time she would stop and speak sharply. The Indians believed that her words were from God, released through her by the power of the mushrooms.

Wasson described his visions, which lasted deep into the night. In part he said: "They were in vivid color, always harmonious. They began with angular art motifs, such as might decorate carpets or wallpaper or the drawing board of an architect. They then evolved into places with courts, arcades, gardens—resplendent palaces all laid over with semi-precious stones. Then I saw a mythological beast drawing a regal chariot."

DMT and STP

Psilocybin has never been very popular in this country, mainly because it is less powerful than LSD and because it is difficult to obtain. However, its chemical cousin, dimethyltriptamine (DMT), is the super-hallucogen. Its power dwarfs that of LSD, and for that reason, as well as for the brief duration of its effect— it lasts about 45 minutes—it is popular among hippies, particularly the plastic or weekend types. DET or diethyltryptamine, related to DMT is another short-haul drug that has some popularity.

DMT is one of the easiest hallucogens for chemists to make at home, and the powder—which is reddish, yellowish, orange or, in its purest form, white—can be mixed with marijuana or pipe tobacco or soaked into parsley as well as be injected. It is true that this mind-bender must be taken in larger amounts than LSD to achieve the same effects. But the brief ride has all the thrills of riding a roller coaster while climbing from one car to another—at least until the crossbeams smash the mind.

In *Nightmare Drugs,* Louria relates this story of one DMT user: "I entered into an experience of unimaginable power. Waves of feeling swept up from my feet to engulf me; lighting flashes traveled throughout my body, seemingly inside my veins and arteries." Then the user was disturbed by someone else who was present in the room: "[the intrusion] precipitated a swift, terrifying and dizzying descent through a black, whirling eddy, twisting and spinning in endless space into a microscopic world where I became an egoless, formless, cellular creature in a world of oozing organisims—a pre-evolutionary time of primeval ooz and incredible fear. I felt beyond death in a hell even Dante did not imagine."

STP to many is an oil additive, but to the hippies on the West Coast it is another drug whose power and effects make LSD look like pablum. STP is the Dow Chemical Company's DOM, an experimental compound currently being tested in the hope that it might be used to treat some forms of mental illness. Somehow, directions for making DOM slipped out of Dow's Walnut Creek Research Center near San Francisco. Hippies quickly realized that DOM could really turn on the human motor, so they named their drug after the oil additive.

STP is similar to the hallucogenic mescaline combined with the stimulant amphetamine. It can produce a 72-hour trip, six times the length effected by LSD. It generates the blinding white light of hallucinatory omniscience that hippies feel is the end-all of the drug experience. Unlike LSD, bad trips on STP cannot be controlled with tranquilizers, inasmuch as they only heighten the experience.

This caviar of psychedelics has hospitalized many of its users and killed more than a score in its brief history. According to Dr. Frederick Meyers, pharmacologist at the University of California Medical Center in San Francisco, STP users "can get pretty wild." In an interview in the *New York Times* on June 28, 1967, he stated: "The STP users we have seen have had dilated pupils, rapid pulse, dry mouth and blurred vision and give a good picture of atropine poisoning."

A Final Warning

Peyote, mescaline, psilocybin, DMT and STP are but a few of the dozens of hallucogenic drugs available in this country. LSD, marijuana and glue get top billing in the psychedelic world, but an industrious person who is eager to twist his mind out of whack can find just the tidbit to do the trick.

A dabbler in mind-warping drugs is begging for the life of a vegetable. Many find it. Visit them in psychiatric wards. You'll never be tempted again.